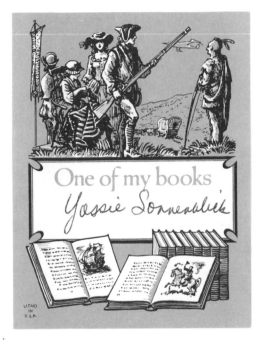

One of my books

Yossie Sonnenblick

The Bar Mitzvah Treasury

THE
BAR MITZVAH
TREASURY

EDITED BY

AZRIEL EISENBERG

BEHRMAN HOUSE, INC · PUBLISHERS · NEW YORK

Manufactured in the United States of America

For my son
Judah Moshe

❦ PREFACE ❧

❧ The quick and eager minds that mark the years of young manhood are probing minds. They ask questions, and demand answers. They are ready to meet—and challenge—the world of ethic, idea, tradition, pattern. This volume, this treasury of creative expression of the ages, was prepared for the Bar Mitzvah, the youth who is being inaugurated into responsible Jewish citizenship, who approaches individual and social maturity, who will be the thinker, the doer, the molder, the leader, the worker, the poet.

The great minds and fluent pens of all ages have always grappled with questions that preoccupy us at the major crossroads of our lives. This book does not attempt to be an answer to these questions. It is, rather, a spirited and meaningful collection of the questions that have been asked, and the ways they have been answered by many different men. The Jewish tradition has always gathered its strength from its constant search for knowledge. In this volume lie Jewish experiences and Jewish thoughts and Jewish attitudes of centuries past and of today. Bring to them your own questionings, your own feelings, and blend them all to find yourself as Jew, as American, and as man.

For ages, men have wondered about God. The first section of this book consists of some of the things men have thought and felt about God for thousands of years. For ages, men have wondered about Man: his behavior, his nature, what is good and what is bad. how man thinks and how man acts. Stories from the Jewish tradition, profoundly concerned with these questions, comprise the section on Man. For ages, men have wondered about Faith: what is Faith, what role does it play in our lives, how can we express it best? In this book you will find the expressions of faith of many men.

One of the sections in this volume is called Torah. It is so called because Torah is not a word, or a book, but an attitude— an attitude firm in the Jewish tradition—of study, search, and learning. Stories and essays reveal with warmth and love the place of Torah in the Jewish past and present.

As Jewish Americans, we are historically involved with the story of the people who lived in the land called Palestine more than two thousand years ago. It was there that our traditions had its beginnings, and it was there, in the Israel of today, that the dream of centuries came true. This wellspring of past and present is the core of the stories in the section called Israel.

As American Jews, we belong to the land in which we live. Writings from the American scene reveal what the United States of America has meant to the Jews, and what the Jews have meant to the United States.

The Bar Mitzvah ceremony is a crucial and dramatic episode in the life of every Jewish youth. In the warmhearted stories and reminiscences of the Bar Mitzvah section, we can see the meaning of this ceremony to other peoples, other times, and to our own day. The Bar Mitzvah Primer touches upon the major areas of Jewish religious observance, and briefly tells of their history and significance.

God, Faith, Man, Torah, Israel, America, Bar Mitzvah: the last is the key to all the others, the inauguration ceremony that is not an ending, but a beginning to the understanding that leads to love of an ancient and ageless tradition and people. This volume begins with the world's greatest book, the Bible. It includes as contemporary a writer as Irwin Shaw. The Bar Mitzvah Treasury is culled from the most exciting and beautiful literature of all times. But behind these stories and essays, as behind all expression, lie many other meanings, meanings which can illumine our minds and our lives. It is my hope that as you close this book, you can say: This is what my forefathers believed, this is how they acted, this is what they felt. I am ready now to draw upon the heritage they left to me, to seek for myself, and in my search to say: This is what *I* believe.

New York, N. Y.   Azriel Eisenberg

∾§ ACKNOWLEDGMENTS ℰ➳ Foremost among the many to whom I am indebted in the preparation of this volume are my publishers, Jacob and Rita Behrman, for their creative role and their stimulation and encouragement. Abraham Segal, friend and collaborator of recent years, has helped in many ways, as have Harold U. Ribalow and Isaac Rivkind. Miss Frances Turner, Mrs. Estelle H. Perl, Mrs. Georgette Gell, and my wife assisted in typing the manuscript.

Many were the friends and colleagues with whom I consulted in selecting the material. I cannot name them all here. Many were there who gave me permission to use selections from their writings which could not be included in the final compilation. I am deeply beholden to them and to the authors and publishers who so generously granted permission to use their material.

Finally, a deep word of appreciation and thanks to my wife, who gave up many an evening and weekend to type and read proof while I was busy at work. Above all, I am grateful to her for having helped bring up two children, one of whom has contributed to this book, and the other for whom the book is intended:

> *Give her of the fruit of her hands*
> *And let her works praise her in the gates.*

A. E.

❧ CONTENTS ❧

ON FAITH

ON TORAH

ON ISRAEL

ON AMERICA

BAR MITZVAH STORIES

BAR MITZVAH PRIMER

I

PROLOGUE

Blessed art thou
O Lord our God
King of the universe
who hast kept us in life
and hast preserved us
and hast enabled us to reach this season.

From the Prayer Book

◆§ WHAT IS YOUR NAME? by Harold Friedman ❧ *There is a word with a very special meaning. For you, for whom this book has been prepared. For this, the thirteenth year of your life. For the deepest and most essential meaning of the ceremony of Bar Mitzvah. The word is* identification. *There are a thousand dictionary definitions for it. But perhaps this little story, about a very little boy, will explain it best. . . .*

◆§ Once, when I was a little boy, I got lost in the May Company—in the handkerchief department.

My mother told me to stay close to her while she shopped for presents. It was Hanukkah time, I remember, and it was raining outside. I let go of my mother's skirt and went to the big front door. I stuck my nose against the door and watched the raindrops sliding down the glass. When I turned around, my mother was gone. And I was lost.

The salesladies were very nice—but I didn't know any of them.

The manager came over and he was nice, too—but I didn't know him either.

A whole crowd of people came around—they told me not to worry—but I didn't know any of them either.

They were all big people, big people I didn't know, and I was very little. I was frightened and I began to cry.

Then the manager bent down and took my hand and he said, "Little boy, what is your name?"

For a second I kept on crying, and he said it again, "What is your name?"

"Dan Segal," I said.

"My name is Dan Segal," I said. And something wonderful happened. "My name is Dan Segal," I told him, and I stopped crying. I didn't feel a bit like crying any more, I felt warm and good inside. I felt good because I knew my name, and I could tell it. I could say my name and everybody would know who I was. There was nothing more to worry about then; it would be easy to get me back to my mother; everything was all right.

I knew my name, so I wasn't frightened any more.

I knew my name, so I wasn't lost any more.

I was somebody—because I knew my name.

Once when I was a little boy, I got lost in the May Company. But the other day I saw a boy get lost right in our classroom in public school. He knew his name all right—Jimmy Samuels. He even knew his address. But he was lost just the same, as lost as I was in the May Company. At first I didn't understand—well, I'd like to tell you about it.

We were studying about America, I guess. And Miss Statler, that's our teacher, went around the room asking the children, and they stood up and told about the countries their parents or grandparents or great-grandparents had come from, and what their people had done to help build up America and make it a good place to live in, and all interesting things about them. The boy next to me told some interesting things about Holland, and the girl on the other side knew some good things about Ireland, and she even sang an Irish lullaby for us. It was beautiful. And then Miss Statler called on Jimmy Samuels, and Jimmy just sat there.

Miss Statler looked at him; she said: "Jimmy, surely you

know something interesting to tell; you're Jewish, aren't you?"

I looked at Jimmy and right away I knew he felt just the way I did that day at the May Company. I could just see it on his face. He got all red, and his eyes filled up, and he looked this way and that just like I did when I was scared and looking for my mother. I couldn't understand why he looked so funny, and then Miss Statler went on and she called on me.

So I stood up and said a few things. I guess I started with how the word Jewish comes from Judah, and he was one of the sons of Jacob and that name sticks in all Jewish history. The kids were listening all right, and Miss Statler nodded to me, so I told a little more of the things I learned in the synagogue —some of the things the Jewish people had done, like getting rid of idols, and fighting to be free from the Egyptians and the Greeks and all the other bad people, and working for the Ten Commandments, and all the fine holidays, and how Sukkot was much like Thanksgiving, and our country was believing in the ideas of the Hebrew Bible, and I guess maybe something about great men in America who are Jews.

I probably talked too long but I learned quite a bit in synagogue—and then all of a sudden, when I sat down, I had a funny feeling. I felt just the way I did when I remembered my name in the May Company, and said it out clear and loud. I felt good inside, all warm and comfortable. I felt just as if I knew my name.

So now I wonder if maybe a person can get lost even if he knows his name and his address perfectly well—if there isn't more than one kind of a name that goes with a person. Seems as if there's a name your family calls you—like Jimmy or Dan.

And maybe there's another kind of name that you call yourself —inside—the kind of a name you get from learning something about yourself and your people, and who you are and where you came from and what's good and useful about you so you feel as good as the next person and understand that they are as good as you. My name is Jewish, that inside name—and I guess I'm lucky, I know that inside name, too.

It's the sort of a name Jimmy Samuels doesn't know, because he never comes to synagogue, and I guess maybe his parents don't care if he looks lost and his face gets red and he looks as if he's going to cry. I wish they would, though. Because you have no idea what a good feeling it is to know your name. To stand up and say it out loud and strong when somebody asks you.

You can't be frightened—when you know your name.

You can't get lost—when you know your name.

You're somebody—when you know your name.

✍ WHY I AM A JEW by Edmond Fleg ☙ *A contemporary French writer reflects on the glorious past of the Jewish people in a great essay. He asks and answers the question: what does it mean to me, that I am a Jew?*

✍ At times, my child, when I go through a museum and stand before the pictures, statues, furniture, arms, crystals, mosaics, vestments, ornaments, coins, jewels, gathered there from all places and all times to hang upon the walls or to place upon pedestals, to be ranged behind barriers and panes of glass, classified, numbered, labeled, I dream that some one of my ancestors may have seen, touched, or admired some of these things ... in the very place, in the very time, in which they were made for use, for work, for the sorrows or the joys of man.

That door with the gray nails, between two poplars, in the gilded frame, is the door of the Synagogue of Geneva through which my father entered to pray. And there, that bridge of boats on the Rhine over which my grandfather in Huningen crossed the river. And his grandfather, where did he live? Perhaps while calculating the mystic numbers of the Kabala in his reveries he saw across the pensive panes of his window, the sleds glide over the snow of Germany or of Poland. And the grandfather of the grandfather of his grandfather? Perhaps he was that weigher of gold in the Ghetto of Amsterdam painted by Rembrandt.

One of my ancestors may have drunk from that wine-cup on returning home after listening to the teaching of his master

Rashi in the School of Troyes in Champagne; one of my ancestors may have sat in that armchair studded with jade when a Sultan bade him feel his pulse; one of my ancestors may have looked upon a monk in his cowl as he carried this cross of Castile while leading him to the auto-da-fé; one of my ancestors may have seen his children crushed beneath the hoofs of the Crusader's horse, who wore that armor.

These crowns of plumes, were they placed in the hands of another ancestor by an American savage? These African ivories, these silks of China, were they bought by another on the banks of the Congo or of the Amur, to be resold on the shore of the Ganges or on the Venetian lagoons?

One of them tilled the plain of Sharon with that plough hardened through fire; one of them ascended to the Temple to offer his tithe in those woven baskets. When this marble Titus was in the flesh, one of my ancestors, chained to his chariot, followed him with bleeding feet in the triumph of the Forum. This bearded magi, with the fringed garment, between these two winged bulls with human profiles—one of my ancestors breathed the dust of Babylon beneath their feet; this Pharaoh of porphyry, with his two hands on his two flat thighs—one of my ancestors bowed himself before his slightest breath, before girding his loins and taking his staff in hand to follow Moses across the Red Sea; and that idol of Samaria, with spherical eyes and triangular jaws, perhaps that was the idol that Abraham smashed when he left his home in Chaldea to follow the summons of his invisible God.

And I said to myself: from that far distant father to my very own father, all these fathers have transmitted a truth to me, which ran in their blood, which runs in my blood; and must I not transmit it with my blood to those of my blood?

Will you accept it, my child? Will you transmit it? Perhaps you will want to desert it. Then may it be for a greater truth if there be one...I could not then reproach you. It would be my fault; for I could not have handed it on to you as I received it. But whether you abandon it, or whether you treasure it, Israel will march on unto the end of days.

From **Why I Am a Jew**, by Edmond Fleg, New York: Bloch Publishing Company, 1933. Translated by Louise Waterman Wise.

II

ON GOD

Once a question was asked of Rabbi Joshua ben Karhah:
Why did the Holy One, blessed be He, choose to
speak to Moses at Mount Horeb out of a thornbush?

Rabbi Joshua answered: "So as to teach us that there
is no place on this earth free of the Presence of God.
God is everywhere, even in the lowly, even in a
thornbush."

Adapted from the Aggadah

⊷§ THE COVENANT ੪∾ Genesis 22:1-19 ⊷§ *Abraham, the first of the patriarchs of the Hebrew people, offers his unquestioning loyalty to the one God in this famous story from the Bible. It is a story from the early history of a young and primitive people. At this time, other peoples practiced human sacrifice. But even the earliest traditions of the Hebrews did not include the Divine right to demand human life as a testament of faith. Abraham shows his willingness to set no limits to his devotion to God. But God did not require this overwhelming sacrifice. Instead, a promise is made: the covenant between God and Abraham. It represents a tremendous advance in civilized thought—leaving behind the primitive custom of the gift of human life, and replacing it with the gift of human faith.*

⊷§ And it came to pass after these things, that God did test Abraham, and said unto him: "Abraham"; and he said: "Here am I." And He said:

"Take now thy son, thine only son, whom thou lovest, even Isaac, and get thee into the land of Moriah; and offer him there for a burnt-offering upon one of the mountains which I will tell thee of."

And Abraham rose early in the morning, and saddled his ass, and took two of his young men with him, and Isaac his son; and he cleaved the wood for the burnt-offering, and rose up, and went unto the place of which God had told him.

On the third day Abraham lifted up his eyes, and saw the place afar off. And Abraham said unto his young men: "Abide ye here with the ass, and I and the lad will go yonder; and we will worship, and come back to you."

And Abraham took the wood of the burnt-offering, and laid it upon Isaac his son; and he took in his hand the fire and the knife; and they went both of them together.

And Isaac spoke unto Abraham his father, and said: "My father." And he said: "Here am I, my son." And he said: "Behold the fire and the wood; but where is the lamb for a burnt-offering?" And Abraham said: "God will provide Himself the lamb for a burnt-offering, my son." So they went both of them together.

And they came to the place which God had told him of; and Abraham built the altar there, and laid the wood in order, and bound Isaac his son, and laid him on the altar, upon the wood. And Abraham stretched forth his hand, and took the knife to slay his son.

And the angel of the Lord called unto him out of heaven, and said: "Abraham, Abraham." And he said: "Here am I."

And the angel of the Lord said: "Lay not thy hand upon the lad, neither do thou anything unto him; for now I know thou art a God-fearing man, seeing thou hast not withheld thy son, thine only son, from Me."

And Abraham lifted up his eyes, and looked, and behold behind him a ram caught in the thicket by his horns. And Abraham went and took the ram, and offered him up for a burnt-offering in the stead of his son. And Abraham called the name of that place Adonai-jireh; as it is said to this day: "In the mount where the Lord is seen."

And the angel of the Lord called unto Abraham a second

time out of heaven, and said: "By Myself have I sworn, saith the Lord, because thou hast done this thing, and hast not withheld thy son, thine only son, that in blessing will I bless thee, and in multiplying I will multiply thy seed as the stars of the heaven, and as the sand which is upon the seashore; and thy seed shall possess the gate of his enemies; and in thy seed shall all the nations of the earth be blessed; because thou hast hearkened to My voice."

So Abraham returned unto his young men, and they rose up and went together to Beersheba; and Abraham dwelt at Beersheba.

⋅§ THE BURNING BUSH ⋅⋅ **Exodus 3:1-15** **⋅§** *God's covenant with Abraham was a living and vital memory. It was reaffirmed to Moses at the burning bush. But this time it was a covenant of all the people. It gave the children of Israel strength. It made a people out of a group of slaves, united under an all-powerful, all-present, and all-knowing God.*

⋅§ Now Moses was keeping the flock of Jethro, his father-in-law, the priest of Midian; and he led the flock to the farthest end of the wilderness, and came to the mountain of God, unto Horeb. And the angel of the Lord appeared unto him in a flame of fire out of the midst of a bush; and he looked, and, behold, the bush burned with fire, and the bush was not consumed. And Moses said:

"I will turn aside now, and see this great sight, why the bush is not burnt." And when the Lord saw that he turned aside to see, God called unto him out of the midst of the bush, and said: "Moses, Moses."

And he said: "Here am I."

And He said: "Draw not nigh hither; put off thy shoes from off thy feet, for the place whereon thou standest is holy ground." And He said: "I am the God of thy father, the God of Abraham, the God of Isaac, and the God of Jacob." And Moses hid his face; for he was afraid to look upon God.

And the Lord said: "I have surely seen the affliction of My people that are in Egypt, and have heard their cry: for I know their pains; and I am come down to deliver them out of the hand of the Egyptians, and to bring them up out of that land unto a good land and a large, unto a land flowing with milk and honey; unto the place of the Canaanite, and the Hittite, and the Amorite, and the Perizzite, and the Hivite, and the Jebusite. And now, behold, the cry of the children of Israel is come unto Me; moreover I have seen the oppression wherewith the Egyptians oppress them. Come now therefore, and I will send thee unto Pharaoh, that thou mayest bring forth My people the children of Israel out of Egypt."

And Moses said unto God: "Who am I, that I should go unto Pharaoh, and that I should bring forth the children of Israel out of Egypt?"

And He said: "Certainly I will be with thee; and this shall be the token unto thee, that I have sent thee: when thou hast brought forth the people out of Egypt, ye shall serve God upon this mountain."

And Moses said unto God: "Behold, when I come unto the children of Israel, and shall say unto them: The God of your fathers hath sent me unto you; and they shall say to me: What is His name? what shall I say unto them?"

And God said unto Moses: "I AM THAT I AM; Thus shalt thou say unto the children of Israel: I AM hath sent me unto you . . . The Lord, the God of your fathers, the God of Abraham, the God of Isaac, and the God of Jacob, hath sent me unto you; this is My name for ever, and this is My memorial unto all generations."

A CALL TO PROPHECY Jeremiah 1:4-19 *The often awesome and thundering proclamations of the Prophets are among Israel's mightiest contributions to the growth of civilized thought. There were certain men in Israel, over a wide span of time in the Biblical era, who saw deeply into the rights and wrongs of the way people lived. Speaking for God, as messengers of God, they spoke against the evils of the time, both in people themselves and in the society in which they lived. They warned; they sought to bring people back to the good way, the way of God. In the history of mankind, the Prophets have done more, perhaps, to shape man's ethical and moral values than any other group; their realization of wrong, and their vision of a better world, still remain in our thinking today. Here are some of the words of the prophet Jeremiah, and his call to prophecy, establishing new relationships between God and His people.*

And the word of the Lord came unto me, saying: "Before I formed thee in the belly I knew thee, And before thou camest forth out of the womb I sanctified thee; I have appointed thee a prophet unto the nations."

Then said I: "Ah, Lord God! behold, I cannot speak; for I am a child."

But the Lord said unto me: "Say not: 'I am a child;' For to whomsoever I shall send thee thou shalt go, And whatsoever I shall command thee thou shalt speak. Be not afraid of them; For I am with thee to deliver thee, saith the Lord."

Then the Lord put forth His hand, and touched my mouth;

and the Lord said unto me: "Behold, I have put My words in thy mouth; See, I have this day set thee over the nations and over the kingdoms, To root out and to pull down, And to destroy and to overthrow; To build, and to plant...."

And the word of the Lord came unto me the second time, saying: "What seest thou?"

And I said: "I see a seething pot, and the face thereof is from the north."

Then the Lord said unto me: "Out of the north the evil shall break forth upon all the inhabitants of the land. For, lo, I will call all the families of the kingdoms of the north, saith the Lord; and they shall come, and they shall set every one his throne at the entrance of the gates of Jerusalem, and against all the walls thereof round about, and against all the cities of Judah. And I will utter My judgments against them touching all their wickedness; in that they have forsaken Me, and have offered unto other gods, and worshipped the work of their own hands. Thou therefore gird up thy loins, and arise, and speak unto them all that I command thee; be not dismayed at them, lest I dismay thee before them. For, behold, I have made thee this day a fortified city, and an iron pillar, and brazen walls, against the whole land, against the kings of Judah, against the princes thereof, against the priests thereof, and against the people of the land. And they shall fight against thee, but they shall not prevail against thee; For I am with thee, to deliver thee."

◦§ THE RELUCTANT PROPHET ◦❧ Selections from the
Book of Jonah ◦§ *Jonah was a reluctant prophet. He tried to
flee from God's will—and could not. Jonah learned that God is
everywhere. He learned too that even though a man may err,
he can always return to God.*

◦§ Now the word of the Lord came unto Jonah, saying: "Arise,
go to Nineveh, that great city, and proclaim against it; for
their wickedness is come up before Me."

But Jonah rose up to flee from the presence of the Lord, and
found a ship going to Tarshish, and went down into it. Whereupon the Lord hurled a great wind into the sea, and there was
a mighty tempest. And the mariners were afraid, and cried
every man unto his god; and they cast forth the wares that
were in the ship into the sea, to lighten it. But Jonah was gone
down into the innermost parts of the ship, and was fast asleep.
So the shipmaster came to him, and said:

"Arise, call upon thy God, that we perish not."

And they said every one to his fellow:

"Come, and let us cast lots, that we may know for whose
cause this evil is upon us."

So they cast lots, and the lot fell upon Jonah. Then they said
unto him:

"Tell us: whence comest thou? and of what people art
thou?"

And he said unto them:

"I am a Hebrew; and I fear the Lord, the God of heaven,
who hath made the sea and the dry land."

Then were the men exceedingly afraid, and said unto him: "What is this that thou hast done?" For the men knew that he fled from the presence of the Lord.

Then said they unto him: "What shall we do unto thee, that the sea may be calm unto us?"

And he said unto them: "Take me up, and cast me forth into the sea; so shall the sea be calm unto you; for I know that for my sake this great tempest is upon you."

So they took up Jonah, and cast him forth into the sea; and the sea ceased from its raging.

And the Lord prepared a great fish to swallow up Jonah; and Jonah was in the belly of the fish three days and three nights. Then Jonah prayed unto the Lord:

> I called out of mine affliction
> Unto the Lord, and He answered me;
> For Thou didst cast me into the depth,
> In the heart of the seas,
> And I said: "I am cast out
> From before Thine eyes;"
> Yet I will look again
> Toward Thy holy temple.
> But I will sacrifice unto Thee
> With the voice of thanksgiving;
> That which I have vowed I will pay.
> Salvation is of the Lord.

And the Lord spoke unto the fish, and it vomited out Jonah upon the dry land.

And the word of the Lord came unto Jonah the second time, saying: "Arise, go unto Nineveh, and make unto it the proclamation that I bid thee." So Jonah arose, and went unto Nineveh, according to the word of the Lord. And he proclaimed: "Yet forty days, and Nineveh shall be overthrown." And the people of Nineveh believed in God; and they proclaimed a fast, and put on sackcloth, from the greatest of them even to the least of them. And the tidings reached the king of Nineveh, and he arose from his throne, and covered him with sackcloth, and sat in ashes. And he proclaimed: "Let neither man nor beast taste any thing; but let them cry mightily unto God; yea, let them turn every one from his evil way. Who knoweth whether God will not turn and repent, that we perish not?"

And God saw that they turned from their evil way; and God repented of the evil, which He said He would do unto them, and He did it not. But it displeased Jonah exceedingly, and he was angry, and he said: "O Lord, was not this my saying, when I was yet in mine own country? Therefore I fled, for I knew that Thou art a gracious God, and compassionate, and abundant in mercy. Therefore now, O Lord, take, I beseech Thee, my life from me; for it is better for me to die than to live." And the Lord said: "Art thou greatly angry?"

Then Jonah went out of the city, and made him a booth, and sat under it in the shadow, till he might see what would become of the city. And the Lord God prepared a gourd, that it might be a shadow over his head. So Jonah was exceeding glad because of the gourd. But God prepared a worm the next day, and it smote the gourd, that it withered. When the sun arose, God prepared a vehement east wind; and the sun beat upon the head of Jonah, that he fainted, and said: "It is better for me to die than to live."

And God said to Jonah: "Art thou greatly angry for the gourd?"

And he said: "I am greatly angry, even unto death."

And the Lord said: "Thou hast had pity on the gourd, for which thou hast not laboured, neither madest it grow, which came up in a night and perished in a night; and should not I have pity on Nineveh, that great city, wherein are more than six score thousand persons that cannot discern between their right hand and their left hand?"

THE STORY OF JOB **Selections from the Book of Job** *How does a man feel when sudden tragedy destroys his whole life—his family, his possessions? He had not wronged any man; he had been faithful to God. Why, then, this punishment? The Book of Job, from the Bible, is the anguish of a man who cries out against fate, and against God. Must the good suffer, and the evil prosper? In his struggle to find the answer for himself, and for all men, Job faces God and glimpses His omnipotence.*

There was a man in the land of Uz whose name was Job. He was God-fearing and he prospered and he was honored among his fellow men. Now God decided to test Job's faith in Him. His family, his wealth, all his possessions, were destroyed. He was smitten with a terrible sickness, and still he held fast to his faith in God. Job's friends heard of the evil that had come upon him, and came to comfort him. For seven days and seven nights they sat with him upon the ground, and none spoke a word unto him, for they saw that his grief was very great. Then Job began to question his misfortunes, and he cried out:

Let the day perish wherein I was born,
And the night wherein it was said:
"A man-child is brought forth."

Why died I not from the womb?
Why did I not perish at birth?
For now should I have lain still and been quiet;
I should have slept; then had I been at rest—

My soul is weary of my life;
I will give free course to my complaint;
I will speak in the bitterness of my soul.
I will say unto God: Do not condemn me;
Make me know wherefore Thou contendest with me.

For the arrows of the Almighty are within me,
The poison whereof my spirit drinketh up;
The terrors of God do set themselves in array against me.

Therefore I will not refrain my mouth;
I will speak in the anguish of my spirit;
I will complain in the bitterness of my soul.
If I have sinned, what do I unto Thee, O Thou watcher of men?
Why hast Thou set me as a mark for Thee,
So that I am a burden to myself?
And why dost Thou not pardon my transgression,
And take away mine iniquity?

Teach me, and I will hold my peace;
And cause me to understand wherein I have erred.

How many are mine iniquities and sins?
Make me to know my transgression and my sin.
Wherefore hidest Thou Thy face,
And holdest me for Thine enemy?
Wilt Thou harass a driven leaf?
And wilt Thou pursue the dry stubble?

Wherefore do the wicked live,
Become old, yea, wax mighty in power?
Their seed is established in their sight with them,
And their offspring before their eyes.
Their houses are safe, without fear,
Neither is the rod of God upon them.
They spend their days in prosperity,
And peacefully they go down to the grave.

Behold, I cry out: "Violence!" but I am not heard;
I cry aloud, but there is no justice.
He hath fenced up my way that I cannot pass,
And hath set darkness in my paths.
He hath stripped me of my glory,
And taken the crown from my head.
He hath broken me down on every side, and I am gone;
And my hope hath He plucked up like a tree.
He hath also kindled His wrath against me,
And He counteth me unto Him as one of His adversaries.

He knoweth the way that I take;
When He hath tried me, I shall come forth as gold.
My foot hath held fast to His steps,
His way have I kept, and turned not aside.
I have not gone back from the commandment of His lips;
I have treasured up the words of His mouth more than my
    necessary food.

❧ Then the Lord answered Job out of the whirlwind:

Where wast thou when I laid the foundations of the earth?
Who determined the measures thereof, if thou knowest?
Whereupon were the foundations thereof fastened?
Or who laid the cornerstone thereof?

Or who shut up the sea with doors,
When it broke forth, and issued out of the womb;
And said: "Thus far shalt thou come, but no further;
And here shall thy proud waves be stayed"?

Hast thou commanded the morning since thy days began,
And caused the dayspring to know its place?

Where is the way to the dwelling of light,
And as for darkness, where is the place thereof;
Thou knowest it, for thou wast then born,
And the number of thy days is great!

Hast thou entered the treasuries of the snow,
Or hast thou seen the treasuries of the hail?

Who hath cleft a channel for the waterflood,
Or a way for the lightning of the thunder;
To cause it to rain on a land where no man is,
To satisfy the desolate and waste ground,
And to cause the bud of the tender herb to spring forth?
Hath the rain a father?

Knowest thou the ordinances of the heavens?
Canst thou establish the dominion thereof in the earth?
Canst thou send forth lightnings?

Who hath put wisdom in the inward parts?
Or who hath given understanding to the mind?

Shall he that reproveth contend with the Almighty?
He that argueth with God, let him answer it!

⇥§ Then Job answered the Lord, and said:

Behold, I am of small account; what shall I answer Thee?
I lay my hand upon my mouth.
I know that Thou canst do everything,
And that no purpose can be withholden from Thee.
Therefore have I uttered that which I understood not,
Things too wonderful for me, which I knew not.
Hear, I beseech Thee, and I will speak;
I will demand of Thee, and declare Thou unto me.
I had heard of Thee by the hearing of the ear;
But now mine eye seeth Thee;
Wherefore I abhor my words, and repent,
Seeing I am dust and ashes.

And the Lord accepted Job, and changed his fortune, and gave Job twice as much as he had before. He had sons and daughters, and much cattle, and many possessions, and the Lord blessed the latter end of Job more than his beginning.

THE SCORPION AND THE SPIDER by Hayyim Nahman Bialik ❧ *The great Hebrew poet of modern times (1873-1934) was also a great storyteller. He reached back into Jewish lore to answer one of man's ageless questions.*

❧ One day while David sat in his garden, he saw a scorpion devouring a spider, and he said, "O God, why hast Thou created these things for naught? The scorpion destroyeth honey but never maketh it; and the spider spinneth the whole year through, yet will its webs never make a garment. What profit is there in them or what pleasure?"

And the voice of God came in his ears:

"David, wouldest thou despise the things which My hands have created? A day will come when thou shalt find great help through them; then shalt thou know that not a thing have I created for naught."

Not many days after, David fled from Saul the King, for Saul sought to take away his life. And David hid himself in a cave in the wilderness. And God ordained for him a spider, and it wove its web over the mouth of the cave and blocked it up. And Saul and his men passed by. One man said,

"Come, let us go and search this cave: it may chance that David is here in hiding."

But another said,

"See, a spider's web, unbroken, is over the mouth of the cave: had any man entered thither the spider's web would be torn to shreds. The cave is surely empty."

And the men turned aside and did not enter into the cave.

When his pursuers were gone a far way off, he left his hiding place, and he saw the salvation which the spider had wrought for him, and he gave thanks and said,

"Blessed be He that created thee! And blessed also art thou, O spider!"

After these things, while Saul was still pursuing after David, David heard that Saul and his men were coming after him into the wilderness. And he knew the place where they were encamped, and he came thither and found Saul lying asleep with his men surrounding him. His spear was thrust into the ground and a pot of water stood by his head; and around him lay Abner and the people. So David came near in secret, and he looked, and, lo, the legs of Abner, as he slept, were bent upright like two pillars, for he was a man of great stature. And David passed beneath them, like as a man passeth between the sideposts of a gate, and entered within the circle of men; and he took the spear and the pot of water from beside the head of Saul. And none saw, and none knew, and none awakened. For they all slept, and the deep slumber of God was upon them. And he turned back to go out; but, lo, Abner stretched out his legs and covered up David, and the legs bore heavily upon him as though they had been two beams: a little more and he had been crushed. David was in very grievous plight, so he cried out to God in his tribulation. And there came a scorpion and it thrust its sting into the leg of Abner, so that Abner again bent his legs upright. And David came out in safety.

Thus David learnt that none of God's works goeth for naught and that a spider can serve as His messenger and a scorpion perform His command.

From **And It Came To Pass,** Legends and Stories about King David and King Solomon, Told by Hayyim Nahman Bialik, Translated by Herbert Danby, New York: Hebrew Publishing Company, 1938.

ᴥ§ GOD'S AGENTS HAVE BEARDS by **Emmanuel Winters** ᶓᴥ *To each of us comes, at some point in our lives, a deep need to confront the question of God. Here is the story of a boy who decided he wanted to meet God, face to face. The author is a writer, critic, and musician, whose short stories have appeared in America's leading magazines.*

ᴥ§ One hot June night after having simultaneously eaten two hundred and fifty peanuts and read two hundred and fifty pages of *The Three Musketeers* by Dumas—which is at the average rate of one peanut a page—I slammed the book shut, stood up to face my father, and announced: "I want to meet God."

Every beautiful, dark-haired, book-loving member of my amazing family, gathered as usual around the dining-room table, stopped reading. Everyone, that is, except my father, who instead of reading had been composing music. For over two hours the only sounds in the room had been the turning of pages, the cracking of brittle peanut shells in the learned, book-salted mouths of my impassioned family, and the scratching of my father's goose quill on the still white music paper before him on the dining-room table. Now everyone stared at me in horror, and there was a ghastly stillness that was broken finally, as expected, by waves of hacking laughter from my tubercular uncle, Amos.

"The boy has gone crazy all of a sudden," he said, simultaneously laughing, gasping, coughing, retching, and finally breaking into tears.

"Amos," my father said, "close your mouth to senseless

laughter. Boys who express interest in God should not be laughed at unless, of course, they express immoderate interest in God." Then he turned to me. "What are you reading?" he asked gently. My father was the gentlest man alive. Sweetness, kindness, and goodness dripped all over him like the warm wax on a great luminous candle.

"*The Three Musketeers*, by Alexandre Dumas," I said. "A very exciting if poorly written book."

My father shook his head. "Very interesting," he said. "Extremely interesting."

Uncle Amos let some more laughter, coughing, and mockery escape from his bitter lungs again. "The boy is *meshugeh*—mad," he insisted. "Here he is quietly reading *The Three Musketeers* by Alexandre Dumas, as generations of us have done each in our turn, and all of a sudden he stands up and says he wants to meet God—and at the same time he gives a book review! Did you ever hear of such a thing before in your whole history of book reading? May I cackle like a jackal full of moldy *potato-kugel* if I ever did!"

"Sure, I've heard of such a thing," my father said. He was quiet and kind, but it was clear that he was thinking hard about this sudden and unlooked-for family crisis.

"Well, I haven't, and if you ask me the boy has suddenly gone crazy from eating too many peanuts," Uncle Amos almost shouted. "That's what he is, crazy from too many peanuts!"

"He's a philosopher," my father said. "Everyone knows it. Otherwise would the very first word he ever enunciated at the age of eleven months and two weeks and three days have been 'why'?"

"He's crazy like a bedbug suffering dyspepsia from the sour blood of an anemic grandmother," Uncle Amos cried.

"Oh, be quiet," my father said. "This emergency calls for some important concentration. Let me think."

Everyone obeyed my father. We were all as quiet as the corpse at a funeral. Nobody cracked peanuts, nobody read, nobody even dared breathe. Except me. I dared do everything with my father.

But this time I was really frightened. The many-mouthed spider of superstition had me in its mandibles. It bit me at page 249. Of course, I had known for a long time what a profound theological upheaval was taking place in my superstitious heart. Every time I walked across town to the great haunted-looking house of Mr. Vladimir Rasputin for my weekly violin lesson, I used to make a deal with fate. "If the toes of my right shoe come out even with the cross lines on the cement side-walk for ten consecutive steps," I used to say, "I'll have a good lesson and Mr. Rasputin won't spit in my eyes and yell: 'Ai, vut a demnt good-far-nahtting boy you are. Ai, you are dr-riv-ing me cr-razy!' " I hoped very hard that my toes would come out even. If sometimes after the fifth or sixth or seventh step the toes would not coincide, once, with the concrete lines, I'd start all over again. Other times I'd try to cheat fate by length-ening or shortening my pace. But if by hook or crook the toes refused to come out even, then I *didn't* have a good lesson.

I had been cogitating on the problem for months. And now, on the eve of going to summer school to skip the sixth grade, I had suddenly realized, on page 249, that perhaps there really was a dark, long-bearded man in the sky who could not be cheated no matter how hard you tried. In that case something had to be done about it right away since summer school started next day, and I had to pass at all costs. Being the official philosopher of the family I always proceeded to logical conclusions. That was why I suddenly felt imbued with a cosmic urge to meet God face to face, if there was such a thing. A grown man of ten has tremendous responsibilities!

So now with the others I waited small and tense for the answer of my gentle and wonderful father....

He was a delight to look at as he pulled his short goatee and concentrated. He was short and stocky, but powerfully built, with broad shoulders that always drove clothing clerks slightly daft. His huge shock of coal-black hair was somewhat interspersed with strands of gray, and his small beard was the same color. By contrast, his forehead was snow-white and high and intelligent. His eyes were a bright dancing blue and his mouth was the gentlest mouth in the whole wide world. I imagined that women would love to kiss that mouth very tenderly. From him there exuded a soft melancholy perfume that was like the fragrance of old and precious books in a bright sunny garden of lilies of the valley.

Finally my father said: "Well, little children, I have decided. The boy's interest in God is not immoderate."

He got up and put on his hat. "Come outside with me," he said, beckoning.

We went out of doors into the warm brilliance of the June evening and began to walk in utter silence.

After we had walked around the block twice without saying a word, my father said: "Now tell me all over again so I'll be sure."

"Pa," I said, "I want to meet God."

We walked around the block once more.

"How do you mean you want to *meet* God? You mean you want proof that there is a God?"

"Excuse me, Pa," I said. "I don't go for second-hand things. I'm a philosopher. I want to meet God personally, face to face."

My father looked amazed. He was wonderful. He didn't say a word. Of course, I knew he wouldn't take me by the left ear and twist my head around. But sometimes if you did something wrong, or, what was worse, something foolish, he would laugh at you in a gentle kind way. This time my father did not even laugh in a gentle way.

We took another walk around the block, then we sat down under a huge elm on the soft sweet grass of June, far away from the lights.

"Do you see the stars up there?" my father asked.

"Yes, Pa," I said. "I see them."

"There's millions," my father said.

"I know it," I said.

"They move exactly on schedule," he said. "They never change."

"Like a clock," I said. This was an old routine.

"Suppose," my father went on, "there was no traffic system to keep the cars downtown moving right. They'd bump into each other all the time."

"Yes," I said.

"Well, there's a traffic system that keeps the stars moving the same way. It's God."

I thought for a while.

"Maybe," I said, "they don't bump each other because they

are so far apart. Maybe once upon a time there used to be more of them, closer together. So they destroyed each other and what's left has all the room it needs. That's why, maybe, they don't bump now."

My father pulled up some grass by the roots and meditated. I did the same.

After a while he said: "Yes, that's possible. It could be like that."

He pulled up some more grass. Then he said: "I want to tell you a story. Once a great idol-worshiping and terrible king told a rabbi that unless this rabbi could produce his God, face to face, in court the very next day, the rabbi's head would roll in the streets. The rabbi said: 'Sure, O great king, but first come on outside in the warm sunshine. I want to show you something.' The king humored the old fellow and went outside. 'Take a look at the sun, O great king,' said the rabbi. The king tried to look. It was a pretty hot sun because this was over in Asia somewhere where the sun's heat is something awful. 'I can't look at the sun,' said this mighty king. 'It hurts my eyes.' 'Well, how in heaven's name do you expect to see God face to face?' said the rabbi, 'if you can't even look at the sun which is only one of the *many* things God has made?' So next day," my father said, "that rabbi was made a vizier or some such almighty thing and from then on until the day he died that king never let the anti-Semites hurt the Jews."

I was pretty quiet for a kid my size.

"Do you get the moral?" my father said.

"Sure," I said. "I get the moral all right, but it doesn't satisfy me."

"It doesn't satisfy you?" my father asked.

"No, Pa," I said.

"Well, why not?"

"Because, Pa, doesn't it say somewhere in the Bible that the old prophets used to speak with God face to face?"

"Yes, it does say that," my father admitted.

"Then why can't I see God, too, face to face, Pa?" I asked.

My father took me by the hand and we got up from the soft green grass and began to walk home. Before we reached the house my father said:

"I'm going to tell you something. But I don't want you to breathe it to a soul, especially not to Uncle Amos." My father wasn't afraid of Uncle Amos. He just didn't like to keep telling him he was wrong all the time.

"Sure, Pa," I said. "I can keep a secret just as good as the next fellow."

"Then," my father said, lowering his voice to a whisper, "if you really want to see God face to face, you can."

"I can?"

"Yes, you can, if you keep asking God long enough and hard enough and God is sure you really mean it."

"You're not kidding me just because I'm only ten years old, are you, Pa?" I said.

"No," my father said. "I never kid anyone—unless it's your mother once in a while."

We started to climb the stairs. "There's something else you should know if you're going to meet God," my father whispered. "Sometimes God's too busy seeing somebody else; then He sends His personal representative. Will that be OK?"

I thought a while.

"Sure, Pa," I said. "I guess that will be OK—so long as I know it *is* His representative."

"You'll know when the time comes," my father said. "But remember, not a word of this to anyone."

"Not a word, Pa," I said.

The next morning at nine o'clock I went down to Union Street School and signed up for summer school. You attended summer school for six weeks and if you passed you skipped a whole grade. That meant a whole year saved.

I was the most ambitious kid in town and I knew that I knew more than anybody else, but I was scared stiff of flunking. That's why I usually came out first in my class. I was so scared of not passing that I worked hard enough to be considered the most brilliant and promising boy in the history of the school system. But being the most promising and brilliant boy in the school system still didn't stop me from being scared to death.

Each day on my way to school I prayed to God to let me pass. "Dear God," I said, "just think of the disgrace to my whole book-reading family if I don't pass the sixth grade in six weeks. My mother will say, "Oh, it was too hard for him," but You and I know it isn't too hard. Uncle Amos will laugh his head off and that isn't too good for his consumption because every time he laughs the blood comes out. So, for the sake of my poor book-devouring family let me pass to my just reward, the seventh grade, O God!" I said it over and over. That was one prayer.

I had a second. "O God," I said, "don't let me waste my valuable time praying to You if You aren't real. Let me see You face to face like the old prophets in the Bible. Just one look, O God!"

I kept repeating this every day. I knew them so well that I was even able to say them under my breath during class.

But I didn't see God. This frightened me all the more since I began to think that maybe God was really there and that He was keeping under cover, out of shame because He had already decided to flunk me. The more frightened I became the harder I studied and I got 100 per cent in all my preliminary exams. But I was still afraid of flunking because the final exam was still to come. I thought that if God was really there, it would be more fun for Him to tantalize me with 100 per cent in the beginning but with a zero in the end. So I kept praying, harder every day.

What made it worse, Miss Regan, my teacher, was fifty-two years old, quite beyond the hopeful stage. Everyone whispered how she once had been in love with a man who, on his way to marry her, had been killed in a railroad wreck. She was skinny and sharp-jawed and always scowled at the kids from way down deep in her rich brown eyes. I felt she was just the type to conspire with God against me.

In fact, the entire summer was vaguely metaphysical.

At length, I took the final examination and was told to report the following morning to find out if I'd passed or not.

That morning I started out for school earlier than usual. I wanted to give myself and God a good last chance. I crossed the South Street bridge, praying hard all the way. As I turned on Washington Street and headed for school, I said: "O God, in just three minutes I'm going to turn the corner at Union where the traffic light is broken and walk into school. You've got just three minutes, O God, to save me and my family from a terrible everlasting disgrace. Incidentally, O God," I said, "those three minutes are important to You, too, because if You don't show yourself to me, then I'll have to stop believing in You, and that means I'll have to stop believing in my father, too, because he said I would see You if I only prayed hard and long enough. So, please God, let me see You now—this minute!"

I stopped walking—scared stiff. If I didn't see God I knew I had flunked. If I saw God—what would I do or say? After all, I had never met God before; He was a perfect stranger to me. But there wasn't a soul on the street, not even a sparrow.

I started walking again, very slowly. Ahead of me was the corner of Washington and Union. Once I turned that it was all over.

"O God," I said, "maybe I've been asking too much. Maybe You're too busy, like my father said. If You are, O God, why not send Your representative? Any old representative will do."

I came to the corner.

"O God," I said. "I'm going to turn the corner now. Send a representative. Let him be right around the corner. Let him have a long black beard. Please, God, please!"

I took a deep breath, clenched my fists, and turned the corner.

There *was* a man there. He *did* have a long black beard.

I didn't know what to do. I just stared wildly at him. When he saw how excited I was, he smiled to me and asked me in Jewish:

"What time is it, son?"

I knew it was just "nine o'clock, O mighty sir," I replied in my best chosen Jewish. Of course, I knew he was checking up on the time so he could tell God what time he had done his job.

He stroked his long black beard, hoisted to his shoulder a huge pack that looked as though it contained carpets, and walked away. I didn't know what to do, so I simply bowed from the waist and watched him until he had turned the corner. Then I went inside.

Sure enough I had passed the sixth grade. I was number one in my class. Miss Regan smiled for the first time in six weeks and said that I was the most brilliant and promising boy in the school system. She said I would have a happy future, but that I must be careful of trains.

That night at home I joined my amazing book-devouring family. In the center of the dining-room table was a fresh, five-pound sack of peanuts. In front of each member of the family was a plate for shells. From the shelf I took down *The Three Musketeers* and opened it to page 251.

On the way to my place at the table I stopped and whispered to my father as he scratched musical notes with his goose quill on a shiny sheet of paper.

"I passed, Pa," I said.

My father nodded his head sweetly.

"I expected you would," he said.

I paused for a while and my father waited patiently.

"I also saw His personal representative today," I said. "He had a long black beard and asked me what time it was."

My father nodded again.

"I expected you would," he said, pulling at his short goatee.

"You two, there, what are you gloating about?" Uncle Amos cried from his couch in the corner. He alone was not reading; he had already read every book in the world in three or four different languages. "If it's something we should know, tell us and stop gloating secretly like two kittens with a bellyful of well-spiced *gefullte* fish," he said.

My father smiled to me and I smiled to him. "It's nothing, Amos," he said gently. "The boy tells me he has passed the sixth grade in six weeks, that's all."

"Well, why shouldn't he pass?" Uncle Amos grumbled. "Haven't generations of us passed the sixth grade—like maggots through the small eyes of a sieve?"

I waited for the family's applause to die down. Then I went to my place at the table and began to read and eat peanuts.

It was still an exciting if poorly written book. But I felt somewhat superior to Alexandre Dumas. He, too, had undoubtedly passed the sixth grade, but had God's personal representative with a long black beard smiled at *him?*

This story appeared in **Harper's Bazaar,** August 1943.

◄§ THE VERY PRESENCE OF GOD by Abraham Rothberg ছ▸

A talented young American writer explores the troubled mind of a new "man in Israel," who leaves his childhood behind and grows toward wisdom and understanding.

◄§ In the small synagogue the high, sing-song cantillations rang clearly in David Hirsch's ears: *"Ma nomar lifonecha yoshav marom."* "O what shall we say in Thy presence, O Thou who dwellest on high?" Beside him his father's voice spoke the Hebrew words that seemed to fall down from his beard. They were coming to the *"Al chait,"* the prayer of recitations of the sins committed during the whole year, the sins that were supposed to be washed away on this Day of Atonement, this Yom Kippur. And now these were his own sins to be washed away, and not his father's, because for the first time on a Yom Kippur he was a man in Israel. Three weeks before he had been "bar mitzvah" and now, confirmed a man, his sins no longer were taken on his father's shoulders. He himself was responsible for them.

But David was not afraid of the sins he had committed and not afraid of asking forgiveness for them in the *"Al chait."* It was after the penitence of the *"Al chait"* that he looked forward to, after it, to the *"Kohanim,"* the priests, and their blessing of the congregation in the *duchanin* ceremony. David had always been told that one did not look up then. Even his father had told him that he was not to look up and it was not only that his father alone had told him. Rabbi Deutsch had told him and Rabbi Eisner had told him too and all the boys at the Hebrew School had discussed it together many times. When the *Kohanim* were praying for the congregation, blessing the people, and the congregation hidden under its prayer shawls with eyes downcast were praying too, no one from the congregation was to look up at the *Kohanim*. Rabbi Deutsch had told them that the *Schechinah* itself—the very spirit and presence of God—was on the altar then and if one looked up with one eye, God would blind him on that eye. If one looked up with the other eye, God would blind him on that eye and if one looked up with both eyes, God would strike him dead. The Rabbi had told them that no one might look upon the face of God and live. Even the great Moses had only been able to see the nape of God's neck on Mount Sinai.

David heard his father begin chanting the *Al chait:* "*Al chait schechatanu* . . . For the sin which we have committed before Thee under compulsion, or of our own will. . . ." His father chanted and automatically David followed with his own *Al chait* striking his fist slowly against his chest for each of the sins committed, as he had seen his father do, for the sins committed "in hardening of the heart." He knew he had hardened his own heart because he wanted to look up to see the *Schechinah* and he was afraid to die, afraid to be blinded and afraid to look up. But he knew still that he wanted to look up.

"For all these, O God of forgiveness, forgive us, pardon us, grant us remission. . . ."

Would God understand and forgive and grant him remission if he looked up? David wondered. Perhaps God would understand that he was not a bad boy, or a disbeliever, that his want-

ing to look was not to disobey but to know, to see if the spirit
of God was really there upon the altar, to see the very presence
of God.

Still automatically, while he was thinking, David read off
the sins for which he wished to be forgiven: "eating and drink-
ing," "usury and interest," "the stretched-forth neck of pride,"
"the conversation of our lips," "ensnaring our neighbors,"
"vain oaths," "causeless hatreds," speaking the Hebrew words
thick upon his tongue and beating his breast with a slow regular rhythm of his right forearm and fist.

"For all these, O God of forgiveness, forgive us, pardon us,
grant us remission...."

When the *Al chait* ended, the voices of the congregation
dropped to a lower pitch and began: "Thy servant David declared in Thy presence, Who can guard against his errors?
Cleanse me, O Lord, from secret thoughts...." David hoped
that the Lord would cleanse him from his secret thoughts, the
thoughts urging him to look up, to watch the *Kohanim* in the
blessing ceremony—and to see the *Schechinah*. Already the
Kohanim were beginning to walk up to the altar, coming from
their seats down the stained red carpeting of the center aisle
and the two outer aisles. They went up the carpeted stairs on
to the darkly polished wooden altar singly and in pairs and
stood silently praying, their striped white-fringed prayer shawls
hanging in limp folds from their shoulders.

The Cantor began to sing, "*Rtzai Adonai Elohenu*...Ac-
cept, O Lord Our God, Thy people Israel and their prayer...."
The congregation was singing and then the Cantor sang and
David could not keep the place in his prayer book. He kept

thinking of the *Schechinah* and the blinding, the finger of God pointing death and blindness at him as he raised his eyes and looked up into the blazing light that was the face of God. All of a sudden he could not see the printed Hebrew characters on the page and his eyelids seemed to stick over his eyeballs as though he could never open them again. *Duchanin* was yet to come and he knew he could not be blinded yet and still he was afraid. He blinked his eyes rapidly, feeling the tears beneath the lids, and then seeing the letters on the page swim quaveringly back into focus. He knew he ought to look up. He was a man now, no longer a boy, and he must know if it were true that the spirit of God stalked on the altar when the Kohanim went up to bless the congregation.

All the *Kohanim* in the congregation were on the altar. The Cantor sang out, his bass voice filling the whole synagogue with its ringing, sounding down from the walls, and sending chills up and down David's spine: *"Kohanim!"*

Immediately David looked down. On the altar he knew that the *Kohanim* were throwing their prayer shawls over their heads and making the split-finger signs of the Hebrew letter *"shin"* beneath them, the letter that stood for the holiest of holy names: *Shaddai!* Loudly, the *Kohanim* sang out the blessing: "Blessed Art Thou, O Eternal! Our God, King of the Universe, Who hath hallowed us with the holiness of Aaron and commanded us in love to bless His people Israel."

The Cantor sang: *"Yivorachicho!"* "May He bless thee."

And David answered with the congregation: "May the Lord Who made heaven and earth bless you from Zion."

"Adonai."

"O Lord, Our God, how excellent is Thy name in all the earth!"

David sang with the congregation, thinking of the *Schechinah* and its presence now on the altar, but not daring to look up to see the *very* presence of God. He kept his eyes glued to the prayer book before him, wondering if he could believe, and doubting.

"Sovereign of the Universe!" David chanted aloud. "I am Thine and my dreams are Thine; I have dreamed a dream, but know not what it portends. May it be acceptable in Thy presence, O Lord, My God!" As he chanted, David thought, I can do it, I can do it, and he exulted. I can get through without looking up and he concentrated on the text of the book, listening carefully, and singing out so loudly that he felt a stir next to him and he could almost feel his father looking down at him questioningly, to see why he was chanting so loudly.

"HIS FACE!" the Cantor sang.

And David found himself again responding with the congregation. "O Lord, hide not Thy face from me; in the day of my trouble, incline Thine ear unto me." And before him the very presence of God was on the altar and he had not yet looked up to see the brightness of the Divine Face.

"Unto Thee," sang the Cantor.

"Unto Thee do I lift up mine eyes, O Thou, Who dwellest in heaven." The congregation sang it and David heard his own voice, thin and still soprano beside his father's low rumbling baritone, and without thought or hesitation, suddenly, he looked up at the altar with his right eye open and his left eye winked closed to look into the face of God. For a moment the

whiteness blazed sheer white and black stripes and then, opening his left eye, he could see the little humps where the *Kohanim* stood, their heads covered over with their white and black-
striped prayer shawls, and the Cantor bent over and then
throwing his head back to sing: "*Sholom.* Peace." Beside him
his father sang and all around him he could hear the congregation: "Peace to him that is afar off, and to him that is near,
said the Lord; and I will heal him."

Then David could no longer hear what they were singing. *He
had looked up!* He had looked on the *Kohanim* and the *duchanin* and he had not been struck blind or dead. Then dully, pound-
ing in his head with the beating sound of his heart, quietly at
first: "...there was no Schechinah...There Was No Schechinah...THERE WAS NO SCHECHINAH!" He blinked his eyes
and put his fingers up to feel them, to see if they were still
there in his head and if he had only imagined that he could see.
But his eyes *were* there, and he *could* see. Again he looked up
at the altar, seeing the *Kohanim* crowded together in the dark,
square, wood-enclosed space of the altar, surrounded by
knobbed banisters, and the Cantor singing with his head
thrown back. There was nothing on the altar that he could see
but the Cantor and the *Kohanim* and their blessing the bowed
heads of the congregation all around him. There was no *Schechinah*, no blindness, no death from looking up.

Finally, the *"Amen, Selah"* rang out and the prayer was over
and the congregation looked up and continued its praying and
David heard his father whisper to him: "Pray! Pray!" Numb
still, he began to speak the Hebrew words aloud in the familiar
rhythm with his father's own cantillation. The afternoon serv-

ice was almost ended. David looked up to where the evening thickened against the outside of the windows, pressing dark and menacingly against the fragile, little shining glass squares. His father nudged him and he began again: "O inscribe us for a happy life. O Thou living God! write us in the book of life; as it is written, 'And ye that cleave unto the Lord Your God are alive, every one of you, this day.' "

The purple curtains, embroidered with the golden lions of Judah standing beside the golden and white embroidered tablets of the Ten Commandments, were drawn aside and the wooden doors of the Holy Ark, in which lay the Holy Scrolls of the Torah, were opened gaping wide.

"This day wilt Thou strengthen us."

"Amen."

"This day wilt Thou bless us."

"Amen."

"This day wilt Thou uplift us."

"Amen."

"This day wilt Thou visit us for good."

"Amen."

"This day wilt Thou inscribe us for a happy life."

"Amen."

"This day wilt Thou hear our cry."

"Amen."

"This day wilt Thou accept our prayer in mercy and favor."

"Amen."

"This day wilt Thou support us with Thy righteous hand."

"Amen," David said to the final prayer and watched the Ark being closed. Then suddenly, unaccountably, he began to cry, softly, in little jumbled sobs. His father heard and turned and said to him in a harsh whisper: "What is it? You're hungry from the whole day's fasting, maybe? You're a big boy now, a bar mitzvah boy, and it's not much longer until the eating."

Still crying David shook his head.

His father grew angry and jabbed an irritated elbow into his ribs: "*Nuh*, what is it then? Tell me! Or stop it! What is it?"

"Nothing," David burst out into a mumbling sob, "nothing." He turned the page in his prayer book to the beginning of the evening service prayers, *Maarev*, for through his tears he could see the evening outside, black against the windows, and just beyond it lay the darkening night.

After Yom Kippur and the blessing of the *Kohanim*, David felt sorry for his parents. His father would get up every morning early and begin putting on the "*tefillim*," carefully winding the black leather thongs around his left arm, after setting the other phylactery over his graying hair and under his dark, silken skull cap. Then, he would say the morning prayer. David did not bother with the *tefillim* and the morning prayer. What good was it? He had looked up to see the presence of God and there had been no presence, and there was no one left for him to pray to. Somehow, it made him feel sorry for his father for believing in such a fairy tale.

David felt sorry for his mother too. Every Friday, as soon as sundown came near, she would set the candles carefully in the three-pronged silver candelabra, polished especially to a shining whiteness, and over her tightly drawn hair the stiff-starched white linen napkin, and she would bless the candles and the incoming Sabbath. David wondered how they could be fooled so easily. They were grown up and knew a great many things, many more than he knew. Why, his father knew all of the Talmud and the Gemorrah, and even mathematics, and he could do David's arithmetic and algebra homework quickly and easily, with different and even better ways than the teacher used.

During the long amber fall days and the white frozen winter ones that came quickly after, David puzzled about it. Perhaps he ought to tell them that he had looked up during the blessing of the *Kohanim.* Perhaps it was wrong of him not to tell his own father and mother. He hadn't told the other boys at the Hebrew School because he knew they wouldn't believe him. Nor could he tell Rabbi Deutsch or Rabbi Eisner. They were holy men. But his own father and mother! He knew he was not a good loyal son but he didn't want to tell them, and the months went by without his ever mentioning once that he had looked up and found the *Schechinah* wanting—and still he could see.

David could see that his mother and father were disturbed by his sudden change toward Hebrew School and the synagogue. Unless he was urged, or scolded, and sometimes actually punished, he did not go of his own accord, and every day there were arguments. Saturday mornings he would sleep late deliberately, and once, when he had arrived at the synagogue so late that half the Sabbath service was over, his father had spanked him for the first time since he was a baby. But David never cried. There was no more sense to crying than to explaining. If he told them that he had looked up and seen nothing, probably they wouldn't believe him anyway; everyone knew that the *Schechinah* was on the altar during the *Duchanin.*

In the mornings when David got up, he would keep his bed-

room door closed and make noises—opening and closing his
bureau drawers and making cantillation sounds with his mouth
—so that his mother and father would think he was putting
on the phylacteries and saying the morning prayers. But he
never said the prayers or put on the phylacteries. Sometimes he
enjoyed the sense that he was fooling them and that it was so
easy but other times it made him sad because they were not
only fooled by that, but by the whole story of the *Schechinah*
and the *Kohanim.* Every day he remembered Yom Kippur and
the strange thumping sound in his head and his heart when he
looked up, the thumping that said ". . . there is no Schechinah
. . .There Is No Schechinah . . .THERE IS NO SCHECHINAH!"
It beat inside him, loud, like a drum lost somewhere in his
chest and head.

In Hebrew School he did not study. He drew pictures of
Rabbi Deutsch or of Rabbi Eisner but he never knew the answers or had the place in the book when they called on him
and his knuckles were growing calloused from the blows of the
ruler which the Rabbis gave when he was unprepared. Each
time he brought his report card home, his mother cried and his
father grew very angry and shouted questions at him without
waiting for an answer:

"Fool! a truck driver you want to be?"

"A C in Torah and a D in Grammar! Are you my son or some
curse from God?"

Then his tone would change suddenly to gentleness and he
would ask:

"Is the work too heavy for you?"

"Do you feel all right?"

"Don't you like Hebrew School any more?"

Then, when David's stubborn silences would enrage him, he would slap him and say:

"You are not just a fool, a *tam*, you are an evil one, a *rusha*."

Passover came. Spring had not yet come and winter had been coldly prolonged into a rainy April. In the streets the bare branches of trees were outlined in silvery-iced slivers and when the lights of the street lamps shone on them they glistened like the silver shine of the candelabra at home. On the first night of Passover though, it was warm inside the house and the table was set. Through the house, David could smell the hot thick smell of potato cakes, the bitter smell of greening herbs, the misty smell of stewing meat, the doughy smell of the matzos. He liked Passover: the food, the wine and seltzer, the songs, the sense of celebration. Most of the other holy days made him feel sad but Passover made him happy. You ate and drank and sang, and remembering the good time he had the last Passover, David didn't mind that he would have to pray, and say the Hagadah, the Passover prayer book.

His mother was making doubly sure that all the things necessary for the ceremony were on the table: the egg, the parsley, the bitter herbs, the matzos, the wine. His father began and soon David had to make *Kiddush*, the blessing of the wine. The Hebrew words seemed strangers to him and he stumbled over them as though he were completely unfamiliar with them. "Blessed art Thou, O Lord, Our God! King of the Universe, Who hath preserved us alive; sustained us, and brought us to enjoy this season."

Suddenly, as they went for the ritual washing of the hands,

David wanted to tell his father about the *Schechinah*. He kept thinking of it when they returned to the table and while they said: *"Ha lachma anya* . . . Lo, this is the bread of affliction, which our ancestors ate in the land of Egypt; let all those who are hungry enter, and eat thereof; and all who are necessitous, come and celebrate the Passover. . . ."* Saying those words made not seeing the *Schechinah* not so important, David thought. He remembered the stories of the Jews in Egypt and their suffering, of Moses, who had seen the nape of God's neck on Sinai, and how Moses had killed an Egyptian he had found beating a Jew. He remembered Rabbi Deutsch's story of the bricks without straw and Rabbi Eisner's story of the ten plagues which were celebrated on Passover. The stories seemed to get mixed up with the *Schechinah* and he began to wonder. . . .

"David!" his mother's voice cautioned him and David could see his father peering over his Hagadah at him, waiting. It was time for the *"Ma nishtana,"* the four questions that the youngest son must ask on Passover. David began the prayer, asking the questions in a small voice:

"Why on this night of all nights do we eat unleavened bread?"

"Why on this night only bitter herbs?"

"Why on this night do we dip twice?"

"Why on this night do we all sit leaning?"

When he had finished and his father was about to begin the recounting of the answers in the *"Avadim hayinu* . . . Because we were slaves unto Pharaoh in Egypt,"* David interrupted. "Father," he said in Yiddish, "I would like to ask you another question." Out of the corner of his eye David could see his mother's warning glance. His father was impatient to get on. He was hungry and there was much prayer to be read before supper began but David would not be put off.

"What is it? *Nuh*, what is it?" his father said gruffly, laying his Hagadah down on the table.

"Everyone says that you mustn't dare look up to the altar when the *Kohanim* bless the people. After I was bar mitzvah, I wanted to look up but the boys in the Hebrew School and Rabbi Deutsch and Rabbi Eisner, they all said that the *Schechinah* was on the altar and if I looked I would be blinded, or maybe killed. They said that God Himself was on the altar, Father. But on Yom Kippur I looked up during the *Duchanin* and there was no *Schechinah;* there was nothing. And I wasn't blinded," he finished lamely, feeling his voice catch and hang trembling in his throat and his eyes were hot with tears so that the candles seemed to be shivering in front of them.

David blinked up at his father and waited, watching his face. Then, suddenly, his father's lined face broke into a broad smile, his white, small teeth showing brightly between his dark mustache and the graying beard beneath. He put his hand out on David's skull-capped head and patted him. "No, David, there was no *Schechinah* there. That is only a story they tell small boys to keep them from looking up. No, the presence of the Lord was not on the altar."

"But why—"

"One doesn't look up because—well, because—it's like the matzos," he said with a sudden inspiration, "it's the tradition not to look up, just as it's the tradition to eat the matzos on Passover because '*Ha lachma anya* . . . this is the bread of our affliction,' and it makes us remember that once our ancestors ate so, this dried and bitter bread," the matzoh crumbled suddenly in his father's clenching fist, "so we try to remember. . . ."

At first the tears came slowly—try as he would David could not force them back—and then faster, like spring rains, and his father said: "*Nuh*, what now?" but David only shook his head and began to read in his quavering voice, with new bass tones sounding in the soprano. "*Avadim hayinu*. . Because we were slaves unto Pharaoh in Egypt, and the Eternal, Our God, brought us forth from thence, with a mighty hand, and an outstretched arm: and if the most Holy, blessed be He! had not brought forth our ancestors from Egypt, we, and our children, and our children's children, had still continued in bondage to the Pharaohs in Egypt. . . ." As David read, his voice deepened and strengthened into a lyrical singsong cantillation because, though he wasn't sure why, the crushed matzoh in his father's fist, breaking into crumbs on the stiff white tablecloth, was an explanation, and a belief.

This story appeared in the New Mexico Quarterly, Winter 1951.

III

ON MAN

How does a man find his Father Who is in heaven?
He finds him by good deeds, and study of the Torah.
And the Holy One, blessed be He, finds man
through love, through brotherhood, through respect,
through companionship, through truth, through peace,
through bending the knee, through humility,
through studious session...
through the service of the masters, through the
        discussion of students,
through a good heart, through decency,
through No that is really No,
through Yes that is really Yes.

From the Midrash

BROTHERLY LOVE *A simple tale of the love of two brothers comes down to us from Hebrew folklore.*

Long, long ago, on the site of old Jerusalem, the holy city, there lived two brothers. They were farmers, and they tilled the land which they had inherited from their father. The older was unmarried and lived alone. The younger was married and lived with his wife and four children. The brothers loved each other dearly and did not want to divide the fields between them. Both ploughed, planted, and harvested the crop together. After they cut the wheat they shared equally in the produce of the earth.

One night during the time of the harvest, the older brother lay down to sleep. But his thoughts were troubled. "Here I am, all alone, with no wife and no children," he told himself. "I need not feed or clothe anyone. But my brother has the responsibility of a family. Is it right that we share our harvest equally? His need is greater than mine."

At midnight he arose and took a pile of sheaves from his crop, carried them to his brother's field, and left them there. Then he returned to his tent quietly and went to sleep in peace.

That same night his brother too could not sleep. He thought about his older brother. "Here I am," he said to himself. "When I grow old my children will take care of me. But what will happen to my brother in *his* old age? Who will take care of *his* needs? It isn't fair to divide the crops equally."

So he arose and took a load of sheaves and brought them to his brother's field and left them there. Then he returned home and went to sleep in peace.

When morning came both brothers were amazed to find their crops exactly as they had been the night before. They wondered greatly but did not speak to each other about this strange event.

The next night each brother repeated his action. When morning came, again they were amazed to find the same number of sheaves as they had left the night before.

But on the third night, when each brother was carrying a pile of sheaves to the other, they met at the top of the hill. Suddenly they understood. Overcome, they dropped their sheaves and embraced and cried with tears of gratitude and happiness. Then they returned to their tents.

The Lord saw this act of love between brothers and blessed the place where they met that night. And when in the course of time King Solomon built the Temple, it was erected on that very spot, from which peace and love flow to the whole world.

This folk tale was set down by Z. Yaavetz, and adapted by Azriel Eisenberg.

⊸§ SAYINGS OF THE FATHERS ⊱ *Wisdom and wit of twenty centuries ago: how true, do you think, are its sharp observations on the ways of human nature today? The Sayings of the Fathers, or Pirke Aboth, are a unique and wonderful collection of maxims, parables, and comments of a group of rabbis from the period of 300 B.C.E. to 200 C.E. Part of the Mishnah, legal code of the Talmud, the Pirke Aboth has been a wise and humane ethical guide for generation after generation.*

⊸§ He [Hillel] used to say, If I am not for myself, who will be for me? And if I am only for myself, what am I? And if not now, when?   I:14

He [Rabbi Akiba] used to say, Everything is given on pledge, and a net is spread for all the living: the shop is open; and the dealer gives credit; and the ledger lies open; and the hand writes; and whosoever wishes to borrow may come and borrow; but the collectors regularly make their daily round; and exact payment from man, whether he be content or not. III:20

He [Rabbi Elazar, the son of Azaryah] used to say, He whose wisdom exceeds his deeds, to what is he like? To a tree whose branches are many, but whose roots are few; and the wind comes and plucks it up and overturns it upon its face; as it is said, And he shall be like a lonely juniper tree in the desert, and shall not see when good cometh; but shall inhabit the parched places in the wilderness, a salt land and not inhabited.

But he whose deeds exceed his wisdom, to what is he like? To a tree whose branches are few, but whose roots are many, so that even if all the winds in the world come and blow upon it, it cannot be stirred from its place; as it is said, And he shall be as a tree planted by the waters; and that spreadeth out its roots by the river, and shall not perceive when heat cometh, but his leaf shall be green; and shall not be troubled in the year of drought, neither shall cease from yielding fruit.   III:22

Ben Zoma said, Who is wise? He who learns from all men. Who is mighty? He who subdues his passions. Who is rich? He who rejoices in his portion. Who is worthy of honour? He who respects his fellow-men.   IV:1

R. Simeon said, There are three crowns: the crown of learning, the crown of priesthood, and the crown of royalty; but the crown of a good name excels them all.   IV:17

There are four qualities among those that sit before the wise: they are like a sponge, a funnel, a strainer, or a sieve: a sponge, which sucks up everything; a funnel, which lets in at one end and out at the other; a strainer, which lets the wine pass out and retains the lees; a sieve, which lets out the bran and retains the fine flour.   V:18

From **Pirke Aboth: Sayings of the Fathers,** edited by Joseph J. Hertz, New York: Behrman House, Inc., 1945.

◁§ **ELEAZAR OF MAYENCE LEAVES A WILL** §▷ *There was a time when people prepared two wills, to be read after their death. One was a distribution of money and property. The other was a testament on living as a man and as a Jew. Eleazar of Mayence, an ordinary Jew, wrote his "ethical will" about six hundred years ago, embodying ideas far ahead of the medieval thinking of the "dark ages." How well do you think it applies today?*

◁§ These are the things which my sons and daughters shall do at my request. They shall go to the house of prayer morning and evening. . . . So soon as the service is over, they shall occupy themselves a little with the Torah, the Psalms, or with works of charity. Their business must be conducted honestly, whether in dealings with Jew or Gentile. They must be courteous in their manners, and prompt to agree to every honorable request. They must not talk more than is necessary; by this will they be saved from slander, falsehood, and frivolity. They shall give an exact tithe of all their possessions. They shall never turn away a poor man empty-handed, but must give him what they can, be it much or little. If he beg a night's lodging, and they know him not, let them provide him with the wherewithal to pay an inn-keeper. Thus shall they satisfy the needs of the poor in every possible way. . . .

If they can by any means arrange it, my sons and daughters should live in communities, and not isolated. . . . Even if compelled to beg the money to pay a teacher, they must not let the young, of both sexes, go without instruction in the Torah. Marry your children, O my sons and daughters, as soon as their age is ripe, to members of respectable families. Let no child of mine hunt after money by making a low match for that object. . . .

As to games of chance, I entreat my children never to engage in such pastimes. During the leisure of the festival weeks they may play for trifling stakes in kind, and the women may amuse themselves similarly on New Moons, but never for money. . . .

I ask, I command, that the daughters of my house be never without work to do, for idleness leads first to boredom, then to sin. But let them spin, or cook, or sew.

I earnestly beg my children to be tolerant and humble to all, as I was throughout my life. Should cause for dissension arise, be slow to accept the quarrel. Seek peace and pursue it with all the vigor at your command. Even if you suffer loss thereby, forbear and forgive, for God has many ways of feeding and sustaining His creatures. To the slanderer do not retaliate with counter-attack; and though it be proper to rebut false accusations, yet is it most desirable to set an example of reticence. You yourselves must avoid uttering any slander, for so will you win affection. In trade be honest, never grasping at what belongs to another. For by avoiding these wrongs—scandal, falsehood, money-grubbing—men will surely find tranquillity and affection. And against all evils, silence is the best safeguard.

Now, my sons and daughters, eat and drink only what is necessary, as our good parents did, refraining from heavy meals, and holding the glutton in detestation. The regular adoption of such economy in food leads to economy in expenditure generally, with a consequent reluctance to pursue after wealth, but the acquisition of a contented spirit, simplicity in diet, and many good results. . . . Accustom yourselves and your wives, your sons and your daughters, to wear nice and clean clothes, that God and man may love and honor you. In this direction do not exercise too strict a parsimony.

Be on your guard concerning vows, and cautious as to promises. The breach of one's undertakings leads to many lapses. Do not get into the habit of exclaiming "God!" but speak always of the "Creator, Blessed be He"; and in all that you propose to do, today or tomorrow, add the proviso, "If the Lord wills, I shall do this thing." Thus remember God's part in your life.

Whatever happiness befall you, be it in monetary fortune or in the birth of children, be it some signal deliverance or any other of the many blessings which may come to you, be not stolidly unappreciative, like dumb cattle that utter no word of gratitude. But offer praises to the Rock who has befriended you, saying: "O give thanks unto the Lord, for He is good, for His mercy endureth forever. Blessed art Thou, O Lord, who art good and dispensest good."

Be very particular to keep your houses clean and tidy. I was always scrupulous on this point, for every injurious condition, and sickness and poverty, are to be found in foul dwellings. . . .

On holidays and festivals and Sabbaths seek to cheer the poor, the unfortunate, widows and orphans, who should always be guests at your tables; their joyous entertainment is a religious duty. Let me repeat my warning against gossip and scandal. And as ye speak no scandal, so listen to none, for if there were no receivers there would be no bearers of slanderous tales; therefore the reception and credit of slander is as serious an offense as the originating of it. . . .

From **Hebrew Ethical Wills**, edited by Israel Abrahams, Philadelphia: Jewish Publication Society of America, 1926.

◄§ **THREE MEN by Mordecai Ben Yehezkel** ᙔ A *Hebrew writer of our times delved into ancient Jewish folklore to find tales with universal meaning and universal appeal. Human problems, human selfishness, human needs, do not change too much. Here, then, is a story of a rich man, a scholar, and a pious man. . . .*

◄§ Once upon a time there lived three townsmen, all of them good and God-fearing. Each followed a different path in life and performed his good deeds in his own way. The first was very rich and famous for his charity. The second was a scholar who spent all his time in the study of Torah. The third was distinguished for his piety, for he worshiped God in awe and in love. And now you shall hear of the strange things that happened to these three men.

As you know, the wheel of fate goes round and man's fortune turns about. At times a man's star will shine brightly and then it will dim and darkness will befall him. This is just what happened to the rich man in our story. For many years he had been very successful in business. He owned a great deal of property: houses and fields and gardens and vineyards. Of course, he lived quite well, but he was also very helpful to his fellow-men. Then suddenly, he lost all his money. Soon there was no food in the house and not even a penny to buy any. The man could no longer stand the suffering of his wife and children, and he decided to seek his fortune outside his town. His wife agreed, and wished him well upon his journey.

The man left his house and walked onto the highway, wondering which way to turn. Then he stopped at a crossroads and waited, hoping to find some other wanderer who might join him. And, indeed, he saw a man with a bundle on his shoulder coming toward him.

This second person was a great scholar, learned in God's laws. For years he had been living on his inheritance, but it slowly melted away, until he was forced to sell his household goods in order to feed his family. He himself continued to study the Torah. But, as our sages have said, where there is no bread, there is no Torah. He began to sell his books, and thus he fed his hungry family. One by one all the books were sold. When the last volume of his treasured library was gone, the man said to his wife: "I have sold everything we once owned. If you agree to my plan, I think I should leave now, and seek my luck elsewhere."

His good wife listened to her husband and said: "May God have mercy upon you and reward your efforts with success."

So these two men waited at the crossroads to see if someone else would join them in their travels. And soon a third man did appear. He was the very pious and God-fearing man. He observed all God's commandments, the major and the minor ones. But he had no peace at home, for he was cursed with a shrewish wife. She swore at him and shamed him, even before others. Finally the good and pious man could no longer endure his life. Without telling his wife, he left. Now he was the third man at the crossroads, and he joined the first two on their travels. They started out by saying: "Let us put our trust in the Name, blessed be He. May He have mercy upon us and see our misery and oppression and help us on our way which we have chosen."

So the three men proceeded together, from city to city, from village to village, always hungry and thirsty. But they found no help anywhere. Three years had passed since they left their homes to seek their fortunes. One day they entered an open field. They stood there under the blue heavens and poured out their hearts before God. They prayed with great devotion and cried to the Holy One from the depth of their souls: "Help us, O Lord, for our troubles overwhelm us." They had not yet finished their tale of woe when, lo! an old man appeared on the road. The stranger spoke to them gently, as though his words were coming from his very heart.

"Why do you weep, my friends?"

They answered: "It is a long story, and it will do no good to tell you of all the things that oppress us, for you can bring us no help. The Holy One alone can redeem us."

But the old man pleaded with them to tell him of their sufferings, and they finally agreed. Each one of the three told his story.

The stranger listened carefully, and he understood their troubled hearts and their tormented spirits. Then he said to them: "All your griefs and sorrows will vanish. You shall each one return to your home and find your families in good health. But you must listen to my advice and do as I tell you. If you will obey me, your lot will be a happy one both in this world and in the world to come."

The old man then took a coin from his pocket and turned to the once-rich man: "My friend, listen carefully to my words. Take this coin, and when you get home, place it in a box. The box will be filled immediately with silver and gold and precious stones. You will possess a great treasure. But you must build

a house of study, fill it with sacred books, and gather together
ten students for whom you will provide generously. Let them
engage in nothing but study. In addition, you will of course
follow in the ways of God and observe all His commandments.
Be sure to give charity to the poor with an open hand and a
gracious heart. If you will do all these things, then you will
always prosper."

Then the old man turned to the scholar and said to him:
"You, too, can now return to your good wife and to your children. But listen to my instructions, and if you will follow them
you will be able to engage in study to your heart's content, for
you will always have all you need. Here is a book. When you
get home put it in your empty bookcase. It will immediately
be filled with books. You will be able to take out volumes and
sell them in order to provide for your family. And if you will
not allow this book of the Torah to depart from your house,
you will raise your children in comfort, and prepare them for
Torah, for marriage, and for good deeds. You must also be
charitable and let others share in your good fortune. Let poor
people be among your visitors, and always feed the hungry."

Then the old stranger turned to the third wanderer, the one
who was known for his piety, and said to him: "All you wish
for is a peaceful home, to have your wife refrain from offending
you both in private and in public, so that you may serve your
God in peace. Here, then, is a ring for you. When you reach
your house put it on a hook on the wall. This ring has the
marvelous power of driving away evil spirits. When a woman
is unpleasant at home, it is an evil spirit that makes her so.
Once this ring is in your home, it will drive out the evil spirit
and peace and quiet will reign forever after. Your wife will bless

you, and all your acts too will be blessed. You will also have
the good fortune of raising a fine family and having great pleasure in them."

The stranger finished his words, turned around, and disappeared.

The three wanderers returned to their city, each one carrying his fate in his hands. When they came to the crossroads
where they had met, they wished each other well, parted, and
went each one his way home.

It was a hot summer day when the once-rich man reached his
house. His wife was outside doing some of her chores. She
lifted her eyes and saw a poor, barefoot man, with torn and
patched clothes. When she recognized him as her husband, the
woman burst into tears.

Then her husband said to her: "My dear wife, pay no attention to my miserable appearance. Listen to the wonderful story
I will tell you." And he told of his meeting with the old man,
and the marvelous coin. "It must have been Elijah the Prophet
himself who gave me this coin," he ended.

The woman could hardly believe her ears, even when she saw
the coin in her husband's hand. But he placed the coin in a
box, and it became filled with silver, gold, and precious stones.
The man and his wife were exceedingly happy. They remembered to do what Elijah had told them. Each day they gave
charity, and they were always ready to help the unfortunate.
The man built a huge palace for himself, as fine as that of any
king. But he did not build the house of study, and he did not
provide for the ten students who were to study Torah.

One day a poor man came to the house of the wealthy one,

asking for alms. Nor was he the only one. There were many others waiting there. When the rich man arrived, he was accompanied by a gentleman with whom he was discussing business. The crowd of supplicants surrounded the rich man, and it was three hours before he could return to his companion and continue their talk. His business associate complained bitterly to him. "Do you think it right to keep me, and others like me, waiting, while you take care of the poor?" he demanded. "You let your own important affairs suffer while you dabble in charity."

After the businessman left, the rich man was gloomy and irritable. He discussed his problem with his wife, and when she suggested that she take care of the charity for him, he consented gladly.

So the rich man now gave all his time to his business affairs, and his wife took care of his charities.

The poor people soon learned that the woman was not nearly as generous as her husband. When they asked to wait to see him, the wife called her servants and ordered the beggars driven away. The servants did so, and the beggars shouted and cried until their wails went up to heaven. Then the woman complained that she could no longer stand the mob of beggars around her house. She advised her husband to ask the mayor to assign two guards to protect his palace. And from that day on, no one was allowed to approach the house of the rich man.

So you see, the rich man forgot all that he was told by the old man who had given him the magic coin.

The second of the three wanderers did not fare much better. That man, you will remember, was a scholar. When he came home he told his wife about all the sufferings he had undergone during the years of wandering, and concluded: "Now we are safe from hunger, and I shall be able to sit in peace and engage in the study of Torah."

The man put Elijah's book in the old and empty bookcase, and lo! it was suddenly filled with many precious volumes. The man sold some of the books to provide for his family, but the bookcase was immediately refilled. The scholar became a great bookseller and gathered much wealth. He built a home, and bought fields and vineyards, and hired men and women to till them and to take care of his household. He prepared a room in which he could sit peacefully and engage in study. But, oddly enough, even though he had a place for study, and no worries, he did not study as much as he had in former days. He was too busy with his business. Nor did he pay much attention to the poor people who came asking for charity. Thus, the scholar too forgot the instructions of the old man who had given him the magic book.

Now as to the third wanderer, the pious one:

When his shrewish wife saw him returning, she shut the door of the house to keep him out. He went to a neighbor and asked him to talk to his wife, to plead with her to let her husband enter. He gave the neighbor the ring he had received, and instructed him to hang it on a nail on the wall. The neighbor did as he was requested. As soon as the ring was in the house, a new spirit came upon the woman. Her voice was soft. She asked her husband to come in, and she treated him with great respect and love. The pious man never became very wealthy, but he and his family lived comfortably and they were happy. He contributed to charity as much as he could afford, and no hungry man would come but that he would leave well-fed and satisfied.

Many years passed, and the three men continued each in his own way. Then one day Elijah came to their town. First he went to the rich man's home. He found soldiers guarding the palace to keep out the poor. When he entered the house, the rich man recognized him, remembered the wonderful coin, and became frightened. Elijah said: "Do you recall how I pitied you and gave you this coin? Did you really think I gave it to you alone? You know very well that I meant you to help the poor and comfort the needy. I told you to build a house of study and to support ten scholars. Where is that sanctuary? You failed to do as you were told. Now you and your family must pay. You do not deserve the precious coin." The rich man fell at Elijah's feet and begged for pity. But Elijah said: "As you have done to others, so shall I do to you." He took the coin and left. All the treasures in the man's home and the palace itself and the property he had around it vanished. The once-rich man was again dressed in shabby clothes.

Elijah then went to the house of the scholar. He found the family at the table gorging themselves with food and drink and enjoying all the earthly pleasures. Elijah spoke to the scholar: "It was not for such things that I gave you the sacred book. It was for the study of Torah and for the observance of its commandments. Return the book to me." And Elijah took the book and went away. And immediately, the bookcases were empty, the money disappeared; everything was gone.

Then Elijah went to the house of the third man, the pious one. He did not find him at home, but his wife invited him to sit at the table, and offered him food. She treated him with kindness. Then her husband came in. He recognized the old man as the benefactor who had given him the magic ring that brought peace to his house. Then Elijah said to the host: "Your fellow-wanderers, the rich man and the scholar, did not heed my warning when I presented them with the coin and the book. They went their selfish ways. But I see that you are as pious and God-fearing as ever. You serve both God and your fellow man. Let me therefore give you the coin and the book. But remember my words: help the poor, build the house of study, and maintain ten students there and provide for them. If you will obey me in all this, you will do well both in this world and in the world to come."

Elijah went his way. And the pious man grew very wealthy and continued to observe all the commandments of the Torah. And the Holy Name, blessed be He, helped him in every way, and he raised a fine family and delighted in them.

This story is from a book of folk tales by Mordecai Ben Yehezkel, **Sefer Ha-Maasiyot,** Volume II (Tel Aviv: Dvir, 1925), and was translated for this volume by Elijah Bortniker.

◄§ THE MESSIAH IS COMING ≈► *Of all the learned schol-ars of the last two hundred years, the name of Elijah, the Gaon of Vilna (1720-1797), stands out as the greatest. In his lifetime he became a legend. Many tales are told about his profound learning, his modesty, and his love for his fellow men. This folk story tells of the Gaon's habit of self-imposed wandering and exile. He would leave his home and go out among the people, learning about their problems, and growing ever closer to them.*

◄§ During one period of his life, Rabbi Elijah, the Gaon of Vilna, took upon himself the penance of wandering through-out the Pale. He went about disguised as a beggar.

While on the road one morning, a Jewish coachman saw the wayfarer plodding along with his heavy knapsack, and offered him a ride.

The sun rose and the day became warm. Rabbi Elijah re-moved his coat, and sat wrapped in *tallit* and *tefillin*, studying Torah, as was his custom.

Soon the coachman said to his companion:

"I feel drowsy, and would like to take a nap. Would you be good enough to take my place on the driver's seat? All you have to do is hold the whip and reins. My horses are well-trained, and know their way."

Rabbi Elijah cheerfully complied with the request. Indeed he was happy to repay the coachman for his kindness. He sat in the driver's seat and held the whip and reins. The driver stretched out on the floor of the wagon, and fell asleep.

Soon they came to a town where a passer-by recognized the famous Rabbi. When he saw the world-renowned Elijah Gaon, driving a wagon, wrapped in a *tallit* and crowned with *tefillin*, he jumped to the only possible conclusion.

He ran to the market place, shouting:

"The Messiah is coming! The Messiah is here!"

All the townsfolk gathered about him, buzzing, asking questions.

"With my own eyes, I saw Rabbi Elijah, the Gaon of Vilna, driving a wagon. Who would his eminence drive, but the Messiah himself?"

The wagon reached the market place. Lo and behold, the report was true! There sat the revered Rabbi in *tallit* and *tefillin*, and in his hands the whip and reins. They all rushed to the wagon to greet the passenger, and saw—the coach driver, fast asleep, and snoring loudly!

Adapted from Hebrew folklore by A. E.

ABOUT RABBI ISRAEL SALANTER *Another leg-endary figure around whom cluster many tales of saintliness and dedication is Rabbi Israel Salanter (1810-1883). The leader of a school of ethical living, his own life was filled with proof of his devotion to the ideal of man's goodness to man.*

Rabbi Israel Salanter, the great and learned Rabbi, was a righteous and pious man. One day, even though there was a full pail of water in the house, he used very little of it to wash his hands. His pupils were quite astonished that their revered Rabbi did not perform properly the commandment to wash thoroughly before eating.

Hesitantly they turned to him and said: "Please forgive us for asking you this. But we cannot understand why you used so little water to wash your hands."

Whereupon Rabbi Israel replied: "I saw that the maidservant delivers this water to the house from a far-off well. She, poor creature, bends low under the heavy load when she carries the yoke on her shoulders. I do not think it right to perform a *mitzvah* at the expense of someone else's shoulders!"

In Kovno, where Rabbi Israel Salanter lived for a time, there was a home for beggars and those who could not afford a night's lodging.

The Home was broken-down and neglected. The inmates lived in dirt and disorder. The trustees hid their eyes from the terrible conditions at the Home. They made no plans to repair it, or clean it, or improve it in any way.

Rabbi Israel Salanter learned of this situation. . . .

He went to the Home one evening, and slept there all night—on the bare floor, together with the other inmates. When morning came, people saw the famous Rabbi leaving the Home.

The shocking news spread through town. That very day the trustees began to renovate the Home and make it livable. Otherwise, how could they face the Rabbi. . . .

Adapted from Hebrew folk tales by A. E.

◆§ REMEMBER THE SABBATH DAY ◈◆ Anonymous ◆§

The Sabbath of the Jews is on Saturday; the Christians, Sunday; the Moslems, Friday. An American story, author unknown, tells how three friends used this difference to help one another. This might be called a modern Midrash, a commentary on the way we do live and the way we can live.

◆§ In a small village in Palestine there lived three friends, a Mohammedan, a Christian, and a Jew. The Mohammedan kept his Sabbath on Friday, the Christian on Sunday, and the Jew, of course, on Saturday.

On Friday the Jew and the Christian set out for their fields. When the Jew saw that the Arab's field was but half-ploughed, he said: "Today my friend can do no work. It is his Sabbath day. Tomorrow it may rain, and he may not have his field ploughed in time for the sowing. I shall plough his field a little, and thereby it may be that his work will be easier for him."

In the meantime, the Christian had said much the same thing to himself, so that, unaware of each other's presence, they ploughed the Arab's field, one from the east, the other from the west.

On the next day, when the Arab came and found his field all ploughed, he wondered, saying to himself, "Who could have ploughed my field? It must be that God has sent His angels to help me."

Months passed by, and the time of reaping came. It was Sunday. The Jew and the Arab had gone to their fields, and the

Christian remained at home to keep his Sabbath. When the Jew saw that his Christian friend's corn was full and ready to be cut, he said: "Today my neighbor cannot cut his grain. Tomorrow a wind may come and scatter his seeds. I shall cut a little for him while I have the time."

Now, strange to say, while the Jew was thinking of his Christian friend's corn, the Arab had the same thought, so that, unseen by each other, they cut the Christian's grain, the Jew from the south, the Arab from the north.

The next day the Christian went to his field, and found the reaping done. He was surprised, and tried to explain it. "It must be that God has sent His good angels to cut my corn for me," he mused.

Reaping time passed and the season of threshing approached. It was Saturday. The Jew remembered his Sabbath day "to keep it holy." The Arab thought to himself: "Ah, the rain is coming, and it is the day of rest of our Jewish friend. Alas! the rain will wash his grain away." And going to his Christian neighbor, he said, "Come, neighbor, let us thresh the grain for our friend, the Jew."

To this the Christian gladly agreed, and after threshing the grain, they bound it up and covered it with straw to protect it from the rain.

When Sunday came, and the Jew set out for his field, he found his grain not only well-threshed, but dry under the straw. Then, lifting up his eyes to heaven, he exclaimed, "Blessed art Thou, O Lord, who dost send Thy angels to help those who remember Thy Sabbath day, 'to keep it holy.' "

◄§ HONEST SCALES by Asher Barash ε► *A contemporary writer in Israel tells of a man who was not the wisest, not the wealthiest, not the most charitable, not the most pious, but who, of all the men in the town, was the symbol of fairness and honesty in the everyday business of life.*

◄§ The synagogue looked like any other synagogue in any town in Poland. But when you entered the vestibule, the first thing you saw was a set of scales in a special glass case opposite the big door. Strangers often wondered at it. It seemed funny for scales to be displayed so prominently in a synagogue. But to the townspeople, the scales had become a tradition. They say that it played its part in saving the whole town from what seemed to be certain destruction.

Many, many years back, a drought had come upon the town. For months, there had been no rainfall. The wells were dry, the land of the surrounding farms was scorched, the skies were like lead, and people suffered. Young and old went thirsty. As the crops began to fail, hunger spread. Disease set in and people died. It seemed as if the whole town was doomed.

The Jews of the town looked for relief to the rabbi, their pious and saintly scholar. The rabbi did what any pious man would do. He prayed. He shut himself up in his room and prayed, day and night. He ordered fast days twice a week, Mondays and Thursdays, according to the Law. He made the rich give charity to the poor. Nothing helped.

One night, long past midnight, the rabbi was sitting alone

in prayer. Suddenly he seemed to fall asleep. As if in a dream, he heard a voice: "Your prayers will bring no help at this time. There is only one man in this town who can help. It is Kalman the grocer. You must summon all the Jews in town to prayer at the Great Synagogue and Kalman must be the cantor. He must lead the whole congregation in prayer."

The rabbi awoke and decided that he had been dreaming. He said to himself, "I have seen this Kalman once or twice in the synagogue. He is an ignorant man, hardly able to read. He is sometimes rude to his customers; sometimes he is quarrelsome.

"Can it really be that Heaven wishes him to be the spokesman for the community?"

And the rabbi decided that after all it must have been only a dream. Again he returned to his prayers. He prayed all day, and all night. Toward morning he fell into a doze. In a dream a voice spoke once more: "Why do you keep on praying when you know that it will not help unless Kalman the grocer will pray for the community?"

This time when the rabbi awoke, he summoned the elders of the city and asked them to announce that every man, woman and child in town go immediately to the Great Synagogue for morning services. Within an hour the synagogue was filled from wall to wall. Everyone sat or stood in silence, waiting for the cantor to go up to the Bimah and begin the service. The cantor remained in his place and so did the rabbi. After a while, the door of the synagogue opened, and Kalman the grocer, the last to arrive, pushed his way in through the door and took his place at the back of the synagogue.

When he saw him, the rabbi rose from his seat, walked over

to him and said, "Kalman, go up to the Bimah. You will be our cantor for today, and lead the congregation in prayer."

There was excited whispering in the congregation. "Why this Kalman?" they asked each other. "Are there not men among us more learned, more deserving of this honor? Why is the rabbi asking this ignorant storekeeper who does not even know the meaning of the prayers to be our cantor?"

Kalman too spoke up. "What are you saying, rabbi?" he protested. "How can I be the cantor when I do not even know how to read?"

The rabbi said, "It does not matter. If you can't read all the prayers, read those that you know. I order you to go up to the Bimah."

But Kalman, instead of obeying, removed his *talith* from his shoulders, placed it on his seat, and without a word, turned and left the synagogue.

The leaders of the community gathered about the rabbi and said, "What will we do now? You can see how ignorant this man is. In spite of your command, he walks out of the synagogue. Probably he does not even intend to return."

The rabbi raised his hand for silence. "We shall wait half an hour," he said, "and then we shall see."

But several minutes later Kalman was back. In his hand he carried the scales he used in his store. Lifting these scales high above his head, he marched straight up to the Bimah while the whole congregation looked on in astonishment.

"What is he doing here with his scales?" people whispered. "Is he going to weigh the synagogue?" And others sneered, "He will probably weigh all of the good deeds he has done in his life."

But now Kalman was standing on the Bimah. Still holding the scales high above his head in plain sight of the congregation, he spoke: "Lord of the Universe, as you know, I am an ignorant man. I have worked hard all my life and have had little time for learning. Sometimes I have been impatient with people. I have often used strong language. I am a poor man and, therefore, have not been able to give too much in charity. But all my life I have been honest, and these scales are the symbol of my honesty. I have kept these scales straight and clean. I have never robbed a customer by giving him short weight. Now, Lord of the Universe, hear me. If I have done no wrong, if my scales have been true, if I have not insulted your Holy Name and have kept sacred the commands of your Torah, I plead with You that You cause rain to descend this very minute, so that we all may live."

The storekeeper finished his strange prayer and in the synagogue there was dead silence. Suddenly a strong wind rattled the windows of the synagogue. The skies grew dark. A moment later, heavy drops of rain could be heard falling steadily on the roof of the synagogue. The town was saved.

Weeks went by, and the rabbi continued to wonder at the miracle. He could not understand why it was Kalman the grocer who had had the power to save the community. True, he had kept honest scales. But there must have been others who were just as honest, just as pious and certainly more learned than Kalman. It took months for the answer to come. Little by little, the rabbi learned the truth. For one by one the merchants of the town came to call on the rabbi. In the strictest of secrecy they confessed that at some time or other, because of carelessness more than anything else, their scales had not always been accurate. It was nothing intentional, they said. It was just that they had not realized how important it was to test their scales and make sure that they were always honest.

When the rabbi learned the truth, he ordered that Kalman's scales be placed in the vestibule of the synagogue, so that every Jew in the town would remember how dangerous small, careless acts can be.

This story appeared in **World Over Magazine,** published by the Jewish Education Committee of New York, February 7, 1947.

◄§ ON PEOPLE by Ludwig Lewisohn &► *The famous novelist and critic, born in 1883, is one of the strong voices on the American Jewish scene today. This tale comes from his novel* The Island Within; *Reb Moshe, one of the characters, relates an anecdote to make a profound point.*

◄§ A man came to a Polish magnate and asked him: "What do you think of the Jews?" The answer was: "Swine, Christ-killers, usurers, not to be trusted." "But what do you think of Isaac?" "A man after my own heart. An honorable man. A kind man. He saved me from bankruptcy." "And what do you think of Berl?" "I have known Berl all my life. He's one of the best." "And of Shmuel?" "Shmuel is a saint as everyone knows."

The same man went to a rich and pious Jew and asked him: "What do you think of the Jews?" The pious man answered: "A kingdom of priests and a holy nation, the elect of the Eternal, blessed be His name." "And what do you think of Isaac?" "That thief? That scoundrel? May his bones be broken. He looks at you and you are robbed!" "And of Berl?" "A fellow of the same kind, without truth or justice." "And of Shmuel?" "Do you think I am taken in by his piety? A pretentious idiot."

Reb Moshe hid his hands in his sleeves: "Avoid both errors."

From **The Island Within,** by Ludwig Lewisohn, New York: The Modern Library, 1928.

◄§ **THE MAN WHO KNEW NO SORROW** by **Hillel Zeitlin** ?► *What are the things that make for a happy life? Is there a quality in man that can turn defeat into challenge, sorrow into joy, obstacles into opportunity? Such a man was Simha the resourceful; simple, content, and with an abiding faith in God. . . . The author, a prominent philosopher, gave his life in the Warsaw Ghetto in 1943.*

◄§ Long, long ago there lived a boastful king. "I am king and supreme ruler of my country," he said. "I have everything I want. Can there be any one happier than I am?"

But a tiny doubt gnawed at this king. Perhaps somewhere in his land there dwelt a happier man. So, one day, he put on the clothes of an ordinary citizen, and traveled up and down his realm, carefully observing the lives of all the people around him. After a long study he decided:

"Indeed, no one is happier than I am. Some possess wealth and property, but have no children. He who has children has no bread to satisfy their hunger. He who is favored with worldly goods *and* children has a shrew for a wife, and she embitters his life. He who is blessed with all three is sickly. And he who is fortunate in having everything—*his* heart is full of fear for the morrow, lest he lose his wealth or his health, or perhaps those dear to him will sicken, or robbers may take away his fortune."

Satisfied, the king was almost ready to return to his capital, when he beheld a small hut with tiny windows and a sagging roof. He looked through the window, and saw a man playing on a violin. The tune was sweet. He looked further, and saw a jug full of wine standing on a table. Every now and then the man poured a glass of wine. Near the jug was a tray of appetizing food. The king studied the man's face, alight with joy and happiness.

The king knocked at the door of the hut. The man admitted him cheerfully, and invited him to join in a repast. He filled a cup of wine and gave it to his guest. Filling another, he drank a toast to the health of the stranger. They feasted and drank until they fell into deep slumber.

When the king awoke, he asked his host: "Who are you, and how do you earn your living, that you can feast and drink and play so merrily?"

"My name is Simha," said the man, "and I mend broken articles. In the morning I go out to the market place and do my work. When I earn my five or six crowns, I buy some good food and return home."

When the king saw the happiness of this simple man, he became filled with jealousy. He began to plot against Simha.

The king returned to his palace and issued a decree: "Henceforth no one may send out any broken articles to be mended. He must either mend them himself, or replace the article."

The next day Simha could not find any work. No one would hire him. For a while his spirits dropped, but he became cheerful quickly.

"God will be good to me," he said. "I have faith in Him."

As he wandered about, he saw a well-dressed man chopping wood for kindling. Simha stopped and said reprovingly: "Is it right that a man such as you chop wood?"

The woodchopper replied: "Indeed not! I could not find anyone to do it for me."

"Let me help you," offered Simha.

So Simha chopped all the wood. His new employer gave him one crown. Simha thanked him, and found other jobs until he had earned six crowns. He bought himself his usual rich repast of food and wine.

Now the jealous king was curious about Simha's fate. He put on his disguise and returned to the hut. Lo and behold, there was food and wine on the table. He knocked, and was admitted. Again he was invited to feast and drink. When he was ready to leave, he again asked how Simha could afford these pleasures.

"You remember I used to be a mender. But now the king has banned mending. So I became a woodchopper and, as you can see, God has been good to me."

Then the king issued a decree that no one could hire anyone else to chop wood, but must do that chore himself.

When Simha went out to seek work, he discovered that his new source of livelihood had been cut off too. His heart became heavy, but his spirits rose again.

"I trust in God," he said.

As he walked through the streets, he saw a man cleaning a sheep pen.

"Do you need help?" Simha asked.

"Indeed, yes," replied the man.

Simha rolled up his sleeves and cleaned out the shed. He received two crowns as payment. The man was so pleased that he told his friends about this good worker. Soon Simha had earned six crowns. He went out, bought his customary repast, and sat down to enjoy his meal.

Once again the king visited Simha's hut, and once again he heard the same story. Determined more than ever to destroy

Simha's happiness, the king issued an edict prohibiting the hiring of labor to clean sheep pens. Then the resourceful Simha hired out as a soldier. During the day he wore a soldier's uniform; at night he received his pay and then made merry with food and drink. Once more the king's plan had failed. Now the king ordered that no soldier be paid daily. When Simha reported to receive his pay the next day, his commanding officer said: "I cannot pay you today. Tomorrow you will be paid for two days."

"But you agreed to pay my wage daily!" Simha complained.

"So I did. But a royal decree banning daily payments was issued today."

For a while, Simha was at a loss. But he thought of a plan. He broke off the steel blade of his sword and replaced it with a wooden blade. He pawned the steel blade, and bought his usual supper of food and wine.

That evening the king went to Simha's hut. He was astonished when he found Simha enjoying himself as always. Simha invited his guest to partake of the banquet and told him all that had happened.

"You recall," Simha added, "that I am an expert mender. Tomorrow night, when I get my wages, I'll redeem the blade, and make my sword as good as new."

"Now," said the king to himself, "I cannot fail!"

The next day the king summoned the commanding officer and issued this order:

"Today you are to execute a man who has plotted against my life. He is to be beheaded. The soldier to behead him must be Simha. No one else!"

Then the king issued invitations to all his officers and counselors to witness the fun—when it would be discovered that Simha's sword was made of wood!

Simha was brought before the king. He fell on his face, trembling: "Why have you summoned me, Your Majesty?" he asked.

"To behead the prisoner who plotted against my life."

Simha implored: "Please do not order me to do this terrible thing! I have never spilled blood in my life. Please, please have someone else do your bidding—a more experienced executioner."

"No," replied the king. "You, only you, are to execute the accused."

Again Simha fell on his face. "Are you certain that the accused is guilty? Perhaps there is some small doubt. I have never spilled blood—not even the blood of a guilty person, let alone the blood of an innocent man!"

Sternly the king answered: "The case is clear. The accused is guilty and deserves to die. The judge has already passed the sentence of death."

Seeing that his pleas went unheeded, Simha looked up, and addressing himself to God, said: "Almighty God! Thou knowest I have never spilled a drop of blood in my life. If the man I am to behead is innocent, may the blade of my sword turn to wood!"

With a flash, Simha removed the sword from the scabbard, and behold, the blade was made of wood!

All the lords broke out into astonished laughter. Vanquished at last and deeply moved, the king said to Simha: "You are a good man. Go home in peace. May God be with you and may you prosper."

Translated by A. E.

❧ PEACE OF MIND by Joshua Loth Liebman ❧ *A famous rabbi in American Israel wrote warmly of the secret ingredient, too often missing from the lives of men, but when present, the clue to the gift of happiness. . . .*

❧ "On my head pour only the sweet waters of serenity. Give me the gift of the Untroubled Mind."

Once, as a young man full of exuberant fancy, I undertook to draw up a catalogue of the acknowledged "goods" of life. As other men sometimes tabulate lists of properties they own or would like to own, I set down my inventory of earthly desirables: health, love, beauty, talent, power, riches, and fame.

When my inventory was completed I proudly showed it to a wise elder who had been the mentor and spiritual model of my youth. Perhaps I was trying to impress him with my precocious wisdom. Anyway, I handed him the list. "This," I told him confidently, "is the sum of mortal goods. Could a man possess them all, he would be as a god."

At the corners of my friend's old eyes, I saw wrinkles of amusement gathering in a patient net. "An excellent list," he said, pondering it thoughtfully. "Well digested in content and set down in not-unreasonable order. But it appears, my young friend, that you have omitted the most important element of all. You have forgotten the one ingredient, lacking which each possession becomes a hideous torment."

"And what," I asked, peppering my voice with truculence, "is that missing ingredient?"

With a pencil stub he crossed out my entire schedule. Then, having demolished my adolescent dream structure at a single stroke, he wrote down three syllables: *peace of mind*. "This is the gift that God reserves for His special protegés," he said.

"Talent and beauty He gives to many. Wealth is commonplace, fame not rare. But peace of mind—that is His final guerdon of approval, the fondest insignia of His love. He bestows it charily. Most men are never blessed with it; others wait all their lives—yes, far into advanced age—for this gift to descend upon them."

He scanned the doubt on my young forehead. "This is no private opinion of mine," he explained. "I am merely paraphrasing from the Psalmists, Marcus Aurelius, and Lao-tse. 'God,' says each of these wise ones, 'heaps worldly gifts at the feet of foolish men. But on my head pour only the sweet waters of serenity. Give me the gift of the Untroubled Mind.'"

From **Peace of Mind,** by Joshua Loth Liebman, New York: Simon and Schuster, 1946.

IV

ON FAITH

The promise God made to Abraham He has kept in the days of our forefathers and in our time. Not one but many have planned to destroy us; indeed in every generation they have arisen against us; but the Lord, blessed be He, always delivers us from their hand.

From the Passover Haggadah

◆§ ELEAZAR SANCTIFIES GOD'S NAME &◆ The Sec-
ond Book of Maccabees &◆ *From the* Apocrypha, *those sacred
and historic writings of the Jewish people not incorporated into
the Bible when it was irrevocably sealed, comes the story of
Eleazar. Part of the Hanukkah legend, for over two thousand
years Eleazar's martyrdom has symbolized a shining faith and
self-sacrifice, to sanctify the name of God. . . .*

◆§ Eleazar, one of the leading scribes, a man of advanced age
and fine appearance, was being forced to open his mouth and
eat pork. But he, welcoming a glorious death in preference to
a life of pollution, went up of his accord to the torture wheel,
setting an example of how those should come forward who are
steadfast enough to refuse food which it is wrong to taste even
for the natural love of life. Those who were in charge of that
unlawful sacrificial meal, because of their long-standing acquaintance with the man, took him aside, and privately urged
him to bring meat provided by himself, which he could properly make use of, and pretend that he was eating the meat of
the sacrifice, as the king had ordered, so that by doing this he
might escape the death penalty, and on account of his lifelong
friendship with them be kindly treated. But he, making a high
resolve, worthy of his years and the dignity of his age and the
hoary hair which he reached with such distinction, and his ad-
mirable life even from childhood, and still more of the holy
and divine legislation, declared himself in accord with these,
telling them to send him down to Hades at once.

"For," said he, "it does not become our time of life to pretend, and so lead many young people to suppose that Eleazar when ninety years old has gone over to heathenism, and to be led astray through me, because of my pretense for the sake of this short and insignificant life, while I defile and disgrace my old age. For even if for the present I escape the punishment of men, yet whether I live or die I shall not escape the hands of the Almighty. Therefore by manfully giving up my life now, I will prove myself worthy of my great age, and leave to the young a noble example of how to die willingly and nobly for the sacred and holy laws."

With these words he went straight to the torture wheel, while those who so shortly before had felt kindly toward him became hostile to him, because the words he had uttered were in their opinion mere madness. As he was about to die under the strokes, he said with a groan:

"The Lord, in His holy knowledge, knows that, though I might have escaped death, I endure dreadful pains in my body from being flogged; but in my heart I am glad to suffer this, because I fear Him."

And so he died, leaving in his death a pattern of nobility and a memorial of virtue not only to the young but to the mass of his nation.

From **The Apocrypha: An American Translation**, by Edgar J. Goodspeed, Chicago: University of Chicago Press, 1945.

🔊 **THE JEWELS by Milton Steinberg** ᓼᕀ *Rabbi Milton Steinberg (1903-1950) was one of the great spiritual leaders of
American Jewry. From his novel of the days of the Romans in
Palestine comes a beautiful story that Jews have retold for centuries. Just as the conflict between the Great Sanhedrin, the
highest Jewish tribunal in the days of the Second Temple, and
the Roman government seemed to be quieting down, the horror
of the plague struck the land. Now the height of it was passed,
but still no one knew where death might strike. . . .*

🔊 On a blazing Sabbath afternoon during this season of calamity, Elisha and Meir sat side by side in one of the synagogues
of Usha. The auditorium baked like the interior of an oven. All
that week the sun had glared with a fury extraordinary even for
a Palestinian summer at its height. Outside now not a breath
of wind stirred, not a wisp of cloud flecked the dimming sky.
But the two men did not feel the heat, nor were they attend-
ing to the speech of a preacher who droned interminably from
the pulpit. They were thinking with unbearable apprehension
of Meir's two sons who even then tossed and moaned in their
little bedchamber. For the fire within them burned ever higher,
parching their skin and glazing their eyes. Physicians, blood
lettings and potions had proved unavailing, and Beruriah, min-
istering to her children with a hypnotic calm, revealed her
desperation only in the pallor of her face and the tonelessness
of her speech.

From a corner of the room the sobs of some bereaved woman
broke forth, shrill and uncontrolled. Meir shuddered at the
sound, and Elisha reached out and pressed his hand. But his

gesture of confidence was only a pretense. Too vividly did he remember the deaths of a young disciple, of a burly laborer on the estate, of an old sage, of a Syrian peddler who dropped in his tracks on the highway before the villa.

"God is just and merciful," he murmured, reassuring himself as well as Meir.

The droning of the preacher came to an end. One of the elders of Usha descended the three steps to a depression before the Ark so constructed that he who prayed for the congregation might literally fulfill the words, "Out of the depths have I called upon Thee, O Lord." In a prescribed chant of great antiquity he called forth the invitation to prayer.

When the brief service was over, the congregants greeted one another hastily and exchanged wishes for a happy week. Then they dispersed, each man to his own home, his own weekday tasks and concerns, or, if so unfortunate, to the sickbed of a kinsman. As Elisha and Meir stepped into the open street, the air, still hot with day, rose from the cobblestones to smite them with an angry hand. A white moon illumined the world with an unreal light.

Meir walked so rapidly that Elisha was barely able to keep abreast of him. He led his teacher into the courtyard of his home and climbed the steps with precipitate haste. The room, when they entered, was silent and dark save for such fragments of the universal whiteness of the moon as poured through its windows.

Beruriah rose from the shadows to greet them. "A happy week to you, my master and husband, and to you, my master and teacher." Her face was a shimmering white mask, its expression inscrutable.

"A happy week," the two men responded.

Then Meir burst forth, "How are the children?"

"Better," Beruriah replied and turned to a cupboard to fetch a lamp, a spice box and a cup of wine.

"It is still the Sabbath here," she said monotonously. "When we have discharged our duty to God we shall talk of our own affairs."

Reassured by her calm, Meir kindled the first light of the new week, pronounced a blessing over the wine cup of division between days, sacred and profane, shook the spice box so that the Sabbath angels might depart in a cloud of fragrance, and uttered the words whereby the week which was about to begin was marked apart from the Sabbath.

The echoes of Meir's last words of prayer had not yet died away when Beruriah began spinning out a parable.

"A man came to see me some years ago," she said in a voice quiet and half-hypnotic. "He left in my care for safekeeping two precious stones. Today, just before you returned, he appeared again. I am loathe to part with them. Tell me, must I give them back to him?"

"Of course," Meir responded guardedly. "They never really were your property, no matter how long you have held them. But why is it so still here? Are the children asleep? Why do you talk of such strange matters?" His voice faded to a whisper, word by word. "Why do you say nothing about the boys?"

Without waiting for answer, Meir turned toward the children's chamber, moved as if to enter and then stopped, struck with sudden comprehension. Like one in a trance, he came back until his face was close to Beruriah's. He stood staring into her eyes, waiting for the interpretation of the parable he dreaded to hear.

Beruriah raised both hands to her quivering lips.

"The jewels," she said, through her fingers, "are in that room."

In the feeble light of the lone flame the face of Meir was transfixed. He pushed abruptly into the children's chamber. For a moment there was only silence behind the swaying curtains. Then through it there cut the horrible rasp of rending cloth. Elisha covered his face. He knew that sound. It was the tearing of a garment in the presence of death.

He did not see Meir when he came out of the room. But he heard with intolerable clarity his stumbling steps and uneven breath. When he opened his eyes again Meir was sinking onto a chair before the table. "The Lord hath given," he droned, "the Lord hath taken away. Blessed be the righteous Judge." He bowed his head upon his forearms and wept.

As though the words of ultimate resignation were a command, Beruriah's hands went to her dress, her fingers tugging at it. The cloth tore under her insistent pulling. With the stiff gait of a sleepwalker, she moved silently into the room where life had been born to her and where, together with her heart, it had died.

And Elisha, to whom these children had become as his own might have been, dug his fists into his chest to keep his tortured heart from breaking.

In the shadows of Meir's home the stillness was broken only by the sobbing of a grown man. A hot wind blew through the open door and extinguished the solitary lamp. For a moment all was darkness. Then the unperturbed moon sent in its spectral light and the room was peopled with creeping shadows.

From **As a Driven Leaf**, by Milton Steinberg, New York: Behrman House, 1946.

◄§ **THE TALLIT WEAVER OF BAGDAD by David Frishman** ᙟᵛ *In the manner of an ancient and lovely fairy tale, the famous Hebrew writer, born 1865, died 1922, tells a story of the powers of God and the reward of faith. Yitzhak was a reasonably happy man, but he had no hope for his own future. One Pesah eve, he had a vision of faith.*

◄§ Long ago in Bagdad there lived a man named Yitzhak—a good and God-fearing man, who was a weaver of *talleitim* (prayer-shawls). Although he worked industriously, he did not earn much money, and his family of ten children dressed in shabby clothes and often went hungry.

But Yitzhak was cheerful and content. He would tell his favorite story over and over. "I do not know what Providence has in store for me, but two things will never come to pass: there will never be a more beautiful *tallit* than mine, and I will never be rich. Poor I was born, and poor I will die." His wife scolded him for his lack of faith, but he laughed and paid no attention to her chiding.

Once, on the eve before Pesah, Yitzhak had finished all his work. Everything was ready for the festival according to law and tradition, and Yitzhak went to the synagogue to welcome the holiday. When the prayers ended, he noticed an old man with a long white beard, dressed in a big fur coat and a wide fur hat. Yitzhak turned to the stranger and asked if he had already accepted an invitation to attend a Seder. The man answered no, and Yitzhak urged him to be his guest.

The old man accepted, thanking Yitzhak for his kindness. Together they walked to Yitzhak's home where they were welcomed warmly. At the Seder table, laden with all the holiday foods, Yitzhak sat on his cushioned stool and leaned back like a king. When they reached the *"Mah Nishtanah,"* Yitzhak told his old joke about the two things that would never happen. The guest looked at him in surprise, but said nothing. As the Seder service continued, the old man began to explain difficult passages of the Haggadah. Yitzhak was delighted with his guest's wisdom: his eyes shone and his heart was glad.

After the Seder, Yitzhak's wife and children, sleepy with all the wine and food, went to bed. But Yitzhak and his guest stayed at the table, discussing the wonders of the exodus from Egypt. Soon the food and wine affected Yitzhak too—his face grew flushed and perspiration covered his brow. The old man suggested that they go out for a walk near the river.

In the midst of their walk, the old man suddenly threw his coat over Yitzhak and wrapped him in it. Yitzhak felt himself being lifted from the earth, and soaring upward. He looked out to find himself flying under the clouds. He heard the old man's voice saying, "Look down, Yitzhak!"

Awed and frightened, Yitzhak looked at the earth below. A marvelous *tallit* was spread before him, such as no human eye had ever seen. The earth, with its dense forests, its rivers reflecting the silver rays of the moon, was a huge shawl. The winding River Hidekel, mirroring the twinkling stars, shone like delicate embroidery. Strips of olive and date trees bordered the fantastic *tallit* like tassels. Never in his wildest fancies had Yitzhak imagined such surpassing tapestry as this, with its elaborate lacework of orchard and garden, vineyard and field, olive grove and park. He was fascinated with the breathtaking, enchanting sight unfolding beneath him.

Then he heard the reproachful words of his companion: "Son of man, now you see the *tallit* that God can weave. So too can He make you rich, if He wills it!"

At these words, Yitzhak felt himself descend. Looking about, he saw he was in front of his house. Bewildered and deeply stirred by his extraordinary vision, Yitzhak went to sleep.

In the morning he asked his wife, "Where is our guest?"

"What guest?" replied his wife, amazed. "We had no guest!"

His puzzled children stared at him, and assured him nobody had come home with him on Pesah Eve. Yitzhak, silent, wondered to himself. Had he then met the prophet Elijah in a dream?

Bagdad was in a gay and festive mood. The princess had been betrothed to the prince of Samarkand, and there was to be a wedding of great pomp and splendor. Everyone looked forward to seeing the princess on her wedding day, when she would wear the wondrous headdress handed down from the generation of the Prophets, and worn by daughters of the Calif.

On the appointed day, the viziers went in stately procession to the mosque where the headdress lay in a vault sealed with seven locks. They removed the seals, opened the vault. Alas! In dismay they found that mice had gotten into the vault and destroyed the lace.

A cry went up throughout the land at this fearful news. All the weavers and lacemakers from miles around were summoned to repair the damage. They tried in vain to restore its delicate and rare beauty. The people despaired, for according to tradition, the bride would have a bright and happy future only if she wore this ancient headdress on her wedding day.

Bagdad had almost given up hope of finding a master weaver to repair the sacred cloth, when the chief of the Calif's bodyguard thought of Yitzhak. He told the Calif about him and Yitzhak was commanded to appear in court.

Yitzhak looked at the tattered headdress. And then, the miraculous vision of Pesah Eve returned to him. The mutilated pattern of the scarf fitted to a thread the marvelous tapestry he had seen in his flight. In his mind's eye he saw again, spread out beneath him, the design of the fabulous *tallit* of God.

Yitzhak spoke to the Calif as if in a trance: "With God's help, I can restore this wonderful cloth. But you will have to provide all the silk I'll need, and see that nobody disturbs me in my work."

Delighted, the Calif agreed. "I will set aside a room in the palace for you. My servants shall provide for all your needs, and no one shall disturb you. If you restore the fabric to its original beauty, I'll reward you with a thousand gold dinars. But if you've only been boasting, and fail to do as you say, I will have you hung!"

Yitzhak had his loom moved from his house to the palace. He ordered silk threads of many wonderful colors. Then he began his work.

At mealtimes the Calif's servants brought him bread and dates, for he was a devout man and would eat only such foods at a strange table. Thereupon the chief cook engaged a Jewish woman to prepare special food for him.

Day and night, Yitzhak worked at his task. Late Friday afternoon, however, he put his work aside, called to the Calif's overseer, and said, "Soon my Sabbath will begin. On this day I stay with my family and do no work, for Sabbath is my day of rest."

The overseer was bewildered. His instructions had been clear: Yitzhak must not be left alone for a moment, nor could he stop work even for an hour.

But Yitzhak insisted. "If you don't let me join my family for the Sabbath, I will not finish the work!"

When this threat reached the Calif's ears, he said, "Let the Jew observe his Sabbath at home with his family. But send two officers along to guard him every moment."

So the guards went home with Yitzhak and stayed beside him the entire Sabbath. They ate the fish and the Sabbath dainties cooked by Yitzhak's wife. They accompanied him to the synagogue. Yitzhak had become famous since the Calif's assignment, and he was honored by being called up to the Torah. As he went, the two guards marched alongside. They waited at the pulpit stairs, and followed when he returned to his seat. Thus Yitzhak spent the Sabbath. After the Havdalah following the Sabbath night service, he returned to the palace.

Yitzhak completed his task in time for the wedding. The new headpiece was a miraculous work of art indeed.

Overjoyed, the Calif gave Yitzhak his full reward, and added to it a new house. Yitzhak raised his children to be honest, God-fearing, and faithful Jews. His new wealth did not spoil his sweet and modest character, and to this day his name is a blessing in the mouths of the people among whom he dwelt.

No longer, now, could Yitzhak repeat his favorite joke. Not only had he woven the most beautiful *tallit* of them all, but he was a wealthy man Both his dreams had come true.

Translated from the Hebrew by A. E.

◄§ **THE PRAYERBOOK by Martin Buber** ও One of the great philosopher-writers of modern times tells a legend of Rabbi Isaac Luria, the Ari, or Lion, the head of a school of Cabbalists. Three hundred years ago, Ari and his disciples dwelt in Safed, a city high in the mountains of Galilee. There they lived as hermits; they tried to hasten the coming of the Messiah and the Kingdom of Heaven by prayer, fasting and good deeds, and magic. To his followers, anything the Ari had touched became a holy and mysterious object. . . .

◄§ It was the custom of the Rabbi of Dynow when he stood up to pray before the Ark of the Covenant on the two High Holy Days, known as the Awful Days, that is, the feast of New Year and the Day of Atonement, to open the large prayerbook of Master Luria (the Ari) and to put it on his lectern. It lay open before him all the while he prayed, though he neither looked into it nor touched its pages, but let it lie before the Ark and the eyes of the people, large and open, so that its strong unblurred black letters glared forth from its wide yellowish background while he stood over it in his sacred office like the High Priest celebrating before the altar. Such was his habit and the eyes of the people saw this time after time but no one of the Chassidim ever dared to speak thereof. Once, however, a few took heart and asked the rabbi: "Master and Teacher, if you pray from the book of Master Luria, why do you not look into its pages and follow the order of its prayers? But if you do not, why does it lie open before you all the time?" And the rabbi said to them: "I will tell you something that happened in the days of the holy Baal Shem, blessed be his memory.

"In a certain village there lived a Jewish landholder with his wife and little son. The lord of the manor was fond of him, for he was a quiet man, and granted him many favors. Evil days, however, came on him. Summer after summer bad crops followed, and want grew and swelled in his house, till the grey waves of misery dashed over his head. He had held his own against hard work and poverty, but beggary he could not face. He felt that his life was ebbing away, and when his heart stopped at last it was like the dying of a pendulum-swing whose steady slowing passes unnoticed until its final lull seems to take one by surprise. His wife, who had passed with him through the good and evil days of his fortune, soon followed him. When he was buried, she could no longer restrain herself; she looked at her young son and not even then could she smother her longing for her dead husband. So she lay down, saying to herself all the time that she was not going to die— till she was dead.

"Little Nachum was three years old when his parents died. They had come from a faraway country and no one knew their kinsmen. So the lord of the manor took him into his house, for the boy with his small face shimmering blossom-white out of his golden locks found grace in his eyes. He soon came to love more and more this delicate, dreamy child, and brought him up as his own. And thus the boy grew in light and joy, and was taught in all the arts and sciences. Of the faith and nation of his parents he knew nothing. Not that his foster-father kept from him the knowledge that his father and mother had been Jews, but when speaking of this he would always add: 'But I have taken you and you are now my son and what is mine shall be yours.' This Nachum could well understand, but what was said of his parents seemed to him to be one of those fairy tales told by the servants, stories of woodspirits, mermaids, and gay elfin folk. That he himself should be involved in such a story was dark and wonderful to his mind, and he felt wrapt in a strange twilight, and fear and longing arose in him, a yearning which seemed at times to bathe his soul in light dreamy waves, which was always weird and marvelous to him.

"One day he suddenly came upon a deserted room of the house, where there lay a heap of things which his parents had left behind. Strange and unknown these were to him. He saw a curious loose white tunic with long black stripes; a woven kerchief of fine yet simple workmanship; a large, many-branched candelabrum of faded splendor; a richly-chased, crown-shaped spice box, about which there still seemed to linger a faint aroma. And there was finally a large thick book bound in dark brown faded velvet with silver-trimmed edges and silver clasps. These were things which his parents could not part from even in the extreme of poverty. And little Nachum stood and looked at them, and the messengers of dusk seemed nearer than ever around him. Then he took the book, shyly and carefully, and clasping it with both arms he carried it to his room. There he unfastened the clasps and opened it wide. The large black letters stared at him, strange and yet familiar, winked at him like a group of young friends, beckoned to him like a cluster of dancing playmates, whirled around him, twined through the pages, flew up and down, swam before his eyes—and lo! the letters vanished, the book was like to a dark sea, and two eyes gazed at him from its depth, tearless yet full of eternal sadness. And Nachum knew that this was the book from which his mother had prayed. From that day on he kept it hidden in the daytime but every night would take it out from its hiding-place and, by the light of the lamp or, better, by the living light of the moon, he would look at the strange letters which danced before him and flowed into a sea whence the eyes of his mother gazed at him.

"And thus came the days of judgment, the days of grace, the Awful Days. From many villages Jews traveled to the city to stand before God with the clamor of the multitude, to bring him their sins together with the sins of thousands and burn them on the fire of His mercy. Nachum was standing by the door of his house and saw numberless wagons hurry by, saw men and women in festive garments, and a spirit of expectancy over all. And he thought that these were messengers to him, no longer envoys of darkness but of light now and peace of soul, and that they passed him by because he failed to hail them. And he stopped one of them and asked him: 'Where are you going, and what day is this for you?' And the man answered and said: 'We are going to the Day of Rebirth, the Day of Beginning, when our deeds and their forgiveness are recorded in the Book of Heaven. And now we journey to plead to God in great multitude and to join our voices into one prayer.' The boy heard these words but, stronger than these, another Word flew to him, a greater Call that came to him out of Eternity. From this hour forth the Call was always with him, roaring in the silence like a mighty stormwind, silent amidst the noise like the winging of a silent bird. And the Call lit up the darkness which had surrounded his world for so long a time, and his fear lost itself in his longing, and his yearning was like to a young green blade in the sun. So passed by the Ten Days of Repentance, and the Day of Atonement was on hand. And the boy saw again the Jews of the villages going on the road to the city. Still and hushed they sat on their carts, and their faces were paler than before. And again Nachum asked one of them: 'Where and why are you going?' And the man said to him: 'This is the day we hoped and waited for, the Day of Atonement, when our sins melt away in the light of the Lord, and he welcomes his children in the House of Grace.'

"Then the boy rushed into his room and took the silver-trimmed book in his arms and ran out from the house and ran till he came to the city. There he directed his steps to the house of worship, which he entered. When he came in, it was the hour of *Kol Nidrei*, the prayer of absolution and holy freedom. And he saw the people standing in their long white shrouds, kneeling and rising before the Lord. And he heard them crying to God, crying from the depth of their hearts to the Light, cry-ing from the hidden places of their souls to the Truth. And the Spirit of God touched the boy, and he bowed and rose before Him and cried unto Him. Then he heard around him the sound of words in a foreign tongue, and he felt that he could not pray like the others. And he took his mother's book and laying it on the lectern before him he cried out: 'Lord of the Universe! I do not know what to pray, I do not know what to say. Here lies before you the whole prayerbook, Lord of the Universe!' And he put his head on the open book and wept and spoke with God.

"It happened on that night that the prayers of the people

fluttered on the ground like birds maimed of wing, and could not soar heavenwards. And the house was full of them, the air was close; dark and gloomy the thoughts of the Jews. And then came the Word of the boy, and, taking all the prayers on its pinions, rose with them to the bosom of God.

"The Baal Shem saw and understood all that happened, and he prayed with great rapture. And when the Atonement Day was over, he took the boy along with him and taught him the meaning of life and all open and secret wisdom."

Such was the tale the rabbi of Dynow told his pious followers. And then he added: "I, too, do not know what to do, and how much to do, and how to achieve the purpose of the holy men who first uttered these prayers. That is why I take the book of our blessed Master Luria and keep it open before me while I pray, that I may offer it to God with all its fervor, ecstasy, and secret meaning."

This story, translated by Simon Chasen, appeared in the **Menorah Journal**, Fall 1936.

THRICE HE LAUGHED by Meyer Levin ❦ *In the eighteenth century in Eastern Europe, the movement called Hassidism came into being. This folk movement was the expression of knowing God through joy and through love. Without books, without study, it was possible for each man to come close to God. Meyer Levin, a renowned contemporary American writer, retells many of the wonderful legends which, along with music, dance, and literature, form the rich heritage of the Hassidim. To Rabbi Israel, the Baal Shem Tov (1700-1760), famous leader of the Hassidim, were ascribed miraculous powers. . . .*

The meal of Sabbath eve was ready upon the table.

Rabbi Israel's head was sunken, and anxiety was deep upon his face. His scholars, seated about the long table, were silent.

The Baal Shem arose and began to speak the blessing over the wine. He lifted his glass.

And all at once a golden shine of joy spread over his cheeks and eyes; he raised his glass, threw back his head, and broke forth in merry laughter. He laughed until he had to wipe bright tears from his eyes.

The scholars could not understand what might have caused the Rabbi's laughter. They looked one to another, they looked at the Rabbi, they looked all about the room. But everything was as always. The candles burned, casting their shine upon the long white tablecloth, and upon the plates that bore the Sabbath meal, and upon the cups of Sabbath wine.

The Master had ceased laughing. But all the sadness was gone from his face. He drank his wine and sat cheerily to his meal.

He began to eat of the fish. Suddenly he set down his hand. His eyes looked far away. And again he broke out into laughter.

During the entire Sabbath, it was the custom of the scholars never to ask questions of the Baal Shem Tov. Therefore they could not ask him the cause of his strange and sudden joy. They ate, and looked one to the other, and wondered.

And when Rabbi Israel was eating soup, he broke out for the third time into laughter. And this time he laughed with the easy contentment of a father watching his children at play.

That night, and all through the Sabbath, the students gathered in groups and discussed the Rabbi's laughter. Three times he had laughed. And they sought in the Torah for explanation of his joy. But they could find no certain answer.

It was the custom of Rabbi Israel in the evening after the out-going of Sabbath to receive one of the scholars into his cabin, and to answer any question that might have arisen among the disciples during the day of rest.

As evening came, the scholars all gathered together and chose Rabbi Wolf from among themselves to go to the Master and ask why he had broken out three times into laughter during the Sabbath meal.

Rabbi Wolf went to the hut in the forest, to which the Baal Shem Tov often withdrew for solitary contemplation. Rabbi Wolf knocked, and entered.

Rabbi Israel asked, smiling, "What questions have the scholars today?"

"They would like to know," said Rabbi Wolf, "why the

Master laughed three times during the meal on the eve of Sabbath."

"Come," said the Baal Shem Tov, "we will get into the wagon and ride, and perhaps you will find out the answer to your question."

Often, on the evening after Sabbath, Rabbi Israel and his students would get into his wagon, and ride on the country roads.

Now they harnessed the horses, and all of the scholars got into the wagon, and all were silent.

The night was soft; it was pleasant. The Baal Shem left the reins lying loosely over his knees. The horses ambled down a forgotten lane. And the Baal Shem hummed to himself, and soon all of the chassidim were humming.

So they rode hour after hour, and instead of turning back they rode onward, and they rode all through the night.

On Sunday morning they found themselves in a village which they had never before seen. Rabbi Israel halted the wagon in front of a tiny synagogue; he got down, and called the shamash.

Soon it was known among all the Jews in the village that the great Rabbi Israel, the Baal Shem Tov, was come among them. Men and women hastened to the market-place, and mothers ran carrying their children to the Rabbi for his blessing, while childless women sought the touch of his hand.

When a great many people had assembled, he said, "Are all the Jews of the village here?"

The head of the congregation looked from one to the other and said, "All."

But Rabbi Israel looked among them as though he sought for

someone; and at last he said, "Where is Sabbatai, the book-binder?"

The shamash ran at once to call the aged Sabbatai. In a moment the shamash returned, followed by a small, grey-haired man, whose blue eyes shone clearly in a mild face.

"Let his wife also be called," said Rabbi Israel.

Then Sabbatai hurried and fetched his wife.

When the two of them were there, Rabbi Israel asked them to stand in the centre of the market-place. On one side of them were all the Jews of the town. And on the other side were Rabbi Israel's scholars.

"Now," said the Master, "tell me, Sabbatai, exactly what you did on last Sabbath eve! But tell me everything, and do not be ashamed, or afraid to speak!"

"Master," said Sabbatai, "I shall indeed tell you everything that happened to me, and what I did; and if it is God's will that I be punished, I am ready to accept the punishment, asking no more than to serve Him."

Then the aged book-binder told his story:

"You must know that since my youth I have lived in this village and practiced my craft as a book-binder. In those early years, when I was filled with vigour, I was able to manage a thriving business, and I lived on all that was best in the world.

"My little wife and I loved to dress well and to have good things to eat, and this we permitted ourselves, for as long as I had enough work to do there was no lack of money. Perhaps we were even somewhat extravagant in buying costly clothing, but my wife was the prettiest girl in the village, and I wanted to see her clothed as became her beauty. And when we drove to the neighboring villages, I too had to be dressed in a way that would not put her to shame.

"So it happened that we spent all the money that I earned, never putting away anything for later years.

"With all that, we led honest and observant lives. From my earliest youth it was the custom in our house to strictly observe the Sabbath. On Thursday afternoon my wife would go to the market and buy fish, meat, flour, candles, and all things that were needed for the Sabbath. On Friday morning at ten o'clock I would put aside my work, close my shop, and go to the synagogue. There I would remain until night fell, when I would go home to the Sabbath meal. Coming toward the house, I would see the lighted candles shining through the window, and I would know that everything was well in my house.

"But during these last years, the weakness of old age has come upon me. I have no sons to help me. And it seems that, little by little, the world is forgetting me. I no longer receive much work from the neighboring villages. And as I am not as vigorous as I was in my youth, I cannot go out to seek more work. Therefore it goes hard with me these years.

"There have been days when we did not have a penny for buying bread. On those days, we fasted. For I said to my wife, 'The people among whom we live are kind-hearted and charitable, and they would be generous toward us if they knew of our plight. But I have lived all my life without asking help of anyone but God, and so I would finish my days.'

"Last Thursday, when my wife was ready to go out to the market, she saw that there was no money in the house, and no food, not even a bit of flour-dust to bake into bread. She came to me and asked me what money i had, but I had earned nothing at all that day. 'Perhaps by tomorrow morning,' I said, 'some work will come into the shop.' Then she went home, and for the first time during our years of marriage, my wife did not do her Sabbath marketing on Thursday afternoon.

"On Friday morning no work came. Then I said to my wife, 'Let us fast throughout this Sabbath. But above all we must not let our neighbors know that we are in need. For the neighboring women would come with meat, and fish, and Sabbath-bread, and you would not be able to refuse their offerings.'

"Then I made a plan, and said to my wife, 'I will tell you how we must manage. I will stay late in the synagogue, later than usual. I will stay until all the others have gone. Then I will be able to come home without meeting anyone who may ask me: "Sabbatai, why are there no candles in your house?" I would not know how to answer such a question. And when I come home at night, we will praise God, accepting what he has given us.'

"So my good wife agreed. And at ten o'clock in the morning I closed the door of my shop and went to the synagogue.

"In our little house my wife sat, and as there was no Sabbath meal to prepare, she had nothing to do. Since she did not like to sit empty-handed, she began to clean the house again. She cleaned the bare table and washed the empty pots, she brushed the vacant cupboard, she swept and dusted where there was no particle of dust, and when she was finished the house was perfect as a jewel.

"Still time went long with her. Then she began to seek for other things to do. And she bethought herself of the great chest filled with old clothing. 'I will put the old clothing in order,' she said, 'and clean it, and mend what needs to be mended.'

"In the chest were all the fine clothes we had worn in our youth. And there among the garments she found a coat that I had worn when we went to the villages to dance, and on that coat were seven buttons covered with gold. My wife was over-joyed! She took her scissors and cut the golden buttons from the coat. She ran with them to the goldsmith. He weighed the gold, and paid her the worth of it in money. Then she hastened to the market. She bought meat, and fish, and flour, and fine tall candles, and she had enough money to buy all the other neces-sities for a perfect Sabbath! Then she went home, and all dur-ing the afternoon she was busy preparing the Sabbath meal.

"When darkness came, and all the others had gone from the synagogue, I walked slowly toward my house. I met no one on the way, and for that at least I was glad, as I thought I would not have known what to say if someone had met me and asked me, 'Sabbatai, why are there no candles in your house tonight?'

"But as I came near the house, I saw the light of candles! Then I thought, my good wife has not been able to withstand this trial, and has accepted the help of neighbors.

"I came into the house. I saw the white cloth spread on the table, and upon the cloth was arranged a beautiful Sabbath meal. I saw fish and meat and fresh-baked Sabbath bread, and soup, and wine for the blessing.

"Then, as I did not want to break the peace and joy of the Sabbath, I said nothing to my wife. I withheld the disappoint-ment that I felt when I thought that she had accepted gifts from our neighbors. I spoke the blessing over the wine, and over the meal, and I sat down to the Sabbath table.

"But after a while I spoke to her as gently as I might, so that she would not feel hurt at my words. I said, 'My good wife, I see that you were not able to refuse the kindness of our neighbors, for you are a soft-hearted woman.'

"But she smiled in a strange joyous way, and laughed at me, and said, 'My honest Sabbatai, do you remember the costly coat you had when you were young, your coat with the golden buttons? Today, having nothing with which to occupy my hands, I searched in the old clothes-chest, and I found your coat. I cut off the buttons and took them to the goldsmith, and he gave me money with which I bought all that we needed for the Sabbath, and there is enough money left for food for another day!'

"Master! My heart was so filled with joy that I could not contain myself. Tears went from my eyes. Once more I praised the Lord for not having forgotten His children. And I praised Him again and again, happy that it was from God Himself, and not from man, that we had received our Sabbath.

"My heart was filled with singing. I forgot the majesty of the Sabbath. And I took my wife by the hands, and led her out, and we danced in our little house. Then we sat down to eat. But when she served the fish course I was so overcome with joy that I took her in my arms and danced with her again. And when we ate our soup, we danced a third time, and laughed and cried for happiness. For my soul overflowed with the glory of God, and I could not shut my heart over the terrible joy that was in it.

"But, Master, it came to me afterward that perhaps our dancing and laughter had disturbed the sublimity of God's Sabbath; and if we have sinned in such a way, and you have come here to find us out, then speak a full punishment over me and my wife, and we will accept it, and do all that remains in our power to fulfill the punishment that you put upon us, and come once more into the grace of God."

So spoke the book-binder, Sabbatai, while his wife stood by his side.

Then Rabbi Israel said to his scholars, and to all who were assembled there, "Know, that all the hierarchy of Heaven sang, and laughed, and was joyful, and danced hand in hand with this aged man and his wife when they were happy on Sabbath eve. And there was a golden joy spread all through Paradise, and joy filled the Eternal Heart. And for the three times you heard my laughter, my friends, I was here with them when they went out three times to dance, and I danced, and I sang with them!"

From **The Golden Mountain** by Meyer Levin, New York: Behrman House, Inc., 1951.

THREE GIFTS by Yitzhak Leib Peretz *A classic tale by one of the greatest Yiddish writers of recent times. Peretz (1851-1915) drew upon the rich sources of Hassidic lore and tradition in his writings, as he did in this story of a soul doomed to eternal wandering, and a grain of soil, a pin, and a thread....*

1 · BALANCING SCALES

Ages ago, somewhere on this earth, a Jew died. Is there anything unusual about a Jew dying? Surely, nobody can live forever! When the Jew passed away, he was buried in accordance with the usual rites.

After the body was laid to rest and the orphaned son said *Kaddish*, the traditional prayer for the dead, the soul winged its way to the heavenly seat of judgment.

On its arrival, it found the scales prepared, on which the court was to weigh all the earthly deeds, the good and the bad.

The advocate of the deceased, formerly his Good Spirit, came up with a clean snow-white bag in his hand and took up his position near the right pan of the scales.

The adversary of the deceased, formerly his Evil Spirit and Tempter, came in with a dirty bag in his hand and took up his position near the left pan of the scales.

The snow-white bag contained good deeds and the filthy black bag evil deeds. When the advocate poured from the contents of the clean bag onto the right pan, the good deeds spread a fragrance of perfume and shone like the little stars in the sky. But, when the adversary poured from the filthy bag onto the left pan, sins came forth black as coal and they smelled of pitch and tar.

The poor soul stood and looked and gaped in astonishment. It never imagined that there was such a wide difference between good and evil, since on earth both often seemed so alike that he easily mistook one for the other.

The pans of the scale moved slowly up and down; now one side ascended and now the other; the pointer of the scale, high about the pans, trembled as it moved a hair's breadth to the left and then a hair's breadth to the right.

Only a hair's breadth and not all at once either! The deceased was a simple Jew, without any great crimes to his debit or any kind of martyrdom to his credit. Petty virtues and petty vices, tiny bits, specks of dust, almost invisible to the eye.

Nevertheless, when the pointer moved a hair's breadth to the right, a tone of joy and exultation resounded throughout the upper regions; but when, alas, it moved to the left, a sigh of sadness broke forth and reached up to the very seat of the All-High.

The angels continued to pour out slowly and faithfully one little particle after another, one speck of dust after another, just as plain people do when they raise the bidding at a charitable auction penny by penny.

Well, even a spring finally runs dry: the bags were empty at last.

"All through?" asked the court attendant, one of the busy angels.

The advocate and the adversary turned their bags inside out: nothing was left. Then the attendant walked up to the scale to see which way it tipped, to the right or to the left.

He looked and looked and found himself confronted with a sight not seen since heaven and earth were created.

"Why do you take so long?" asked the head of the court.

The attendant stammered:

"Even! The pointer has come to a stop in the exact center!"

The good deeds and the evil balanced each other exactly.

"In the very center?" the court queried again.

The attendant took another look and replied:

"Absolutely balanced!"

The supreme court deliberated a while and finally arrived at the following conclusion:

"Since the sins do not outweigh the good deeds, the soul does not belong in hell. On the other hand, since the good deeds do not weigh more than the vices, the portals of paradise cannot be opened for this soul. Hence, the soul must remain homeless. It must fly about between heaven and earth until God remembers it, pities it, and bestows His grace upon it."

The attendant took the soul and led it out of the courtroom.

The poor soul moaned and bewailed its lot.

"Why do you weep?" asked the clerk. "The bliss of paradise may not be yours but then you have also escaped the torture of hell—and so you have broken even!"

The soul, however, refused to be comforted:

"The worst tortures are better than nothingness! Nothingness is terrible!"

The court attendant pitied the poor soul and gave it the following advice:

"Fly down, dear soul, and flutter about the living world. Don't look up to heaven, for what will you see in the sky except stars, luminous but cold, wholly insensitive to pity? The stars will not exert themselves in your behalf. They will not remind God of you and your fate. Only the saints of paradise can plead for a poor wandering soul, and saints like gifts, nice gifts. Such is the habit of saints nowadays," he added bitterly.

"Fly, therefore, O soul, fly down to the living world and observe how it carries on, what it does, and if you see anything of extraordinary goodness and beauty, catch it and fly up with it. Bring it as a gift for the saints in paradise. With this gift in your hand, knock up here and report your presence to the angel at the dormer-window. Tell him I asked you to do so. And after you have brought three gifts, be assured that the gates of paradise will be opened for you. The gifts will be effective. At the throne of the Almighty it is not the souls of the nobly born that are preferred but rather the souls of the upward striving."

With these words the attendant of the heavenly court mercifully sent the soul forth from heaven.

2 · THE FIRST GIFT

◄§ The poor soul flew about, hovering above the living world and seeking gifts for the saints of paradise. It flew over towns, villages and the habitations of men, between burning rays on hot days and drops of rain in the wet season, between silvery gossamer at summer's close and drifting snowflakes at wintertide. It looked and gazed until its eyes almost popped out.

Wherever it saw a Jew, it flew over quickly and peered into his eyes, wondering if he were about to sacrifice himself for his God.

Wherever light seeped through an opening in a shutter, the soul was there and looked in, wondering if God's fragrant flowers were perchance growing in the humble home—good deeds done in secret.

Alas! In most cases the soul retreated from eyes and windows, shocked and terrified by what it saw.

As seasons and years passed by, the soul almost succumbed to melancholy. Cities turned into graveyards and graveyards were plowed under to become fruitful fields. Forests were cut down. Waters reduced stones to sand and rivers changed their beds. Thousands of stars fell down and millions of souls flew upwards. But God was still unmindful of the one soul which still unsuccessfully looked for a gift of unusual goodness and beauty.

The exiled soul brooded: "The world is so poor; human beings have such mediocre gray souls; their deeds are so petty; how can one expect anything extraordinary from them? I am doomed to wander, an eternal exile!"

In the midst of its brooding, a red flame caught its eye, a red flame in the middle of a dark overcast night.

The soul looked about—the flame was shooting up from a high window.

Robbers had broken into a rich man's house, robbers with masks on their faces. One held a burning torch in his hand as a light. Another stood with a glistening knife directed against the victim's breast and repeated over and over again: "A single move, Jew, and you're finished! The point of the knife will come out of your back." The others were opening chests and drawers and removing the contents.

The Jew stood with the knife pointed at his breast and

watched the scene calmly. Not an eyelash moved over his clear
eyes, not a hair of his long white beard stirred. He seemed
wholly unconcerned, as if thinking: "The Lord gave and the
Lord has taken, blessed be the name of the Lord." His pale lips
murmured: "You're not born with it, and you can't take it with
you to the grave."

He looked on calmly, as the last drawers of the last chest
were opened and bags were removed, filled with gold and silver,
with jewels and all sorts of treasures. He looked on and was
silent.

Perhaps he even regarded their loss as his contribution to
fate, which had been so kind to him hitherto.

Suddenly, however, as the robbers reached the last hiding
place and pulled out a little bag, the last and most secret bag,
he forgot himself. He was seized with trembling, his eyes glared,
he raised his right hand to stop them, he wanted to cry out:
"Don't touch!"

But, instead of a cry, a red ray of steaming blood spurted
forth. The knife had done its job. His heart's blood bespattered
the bag. As he fell, the robbers tore open the bag quickly, expecting the best and most valuable loot.

They were, however, bitterly disappointed. In vain had they
shed blood. The bag contained neither silver nor gold nor jew-
elry nor anything of practical value in this world. It had only
a bit of earth from the land of Israel, earth which the Jew had
preserved for his grave. This was the treasure which the rich
man had wanted to save from the hands and eyes of strangers
and which was bespattered with his blood.

The soul catches a bloody speck of this Palestinian earth and
brings it to the window at heaven's gate.

3 · THE SECOND GIFT

◄§ "Remember, two more gifts!" said the angel as he closed heaven's window leaving the soul outside.

"God will help!" thought the hopeful soul, as it flew down again in a more cheerful mood.

This cheerfulness faded, however, as years and years went by and the soul saw nothing of extraordinary beauty. Sad thoughts again came to the fore:

"This world gushed forth from God's will just like a spring of living waters and is now flowing on and on through time. The more it flows, the more earth and dust does it gather, the more turbid and impure does it become, the less gifts for heaven can one find in it. People are becoming pettier, good deeds more minute, sins tinier than specks of dust, actions ever less visible to the eye."

A further thought came to the soul: "If God were to weigh all the virtues and vices of the entire world at the same time, the pointer would hardly budge or vibrate. The world too is incapable of moving up or down. It too is wandering aimlessly between the radiant heaven and the dark abysmal pit. The adversary and the advocate would be fighting over it eternally, even as light contends eternally with darkness, warmth with cold, life with death. The world is in constant motion and yet it can neither ascend nor descend and, for this reason, there will always be weddings and divorces, births and funerals, joyous feasts and fruits of sorrow, love and hate, always, always."

Suddenly, the soul was roused from its brooding by the noise of trumpets and drums.

Looking down, it saw a German city. Slanting roofs encircled the square before the town hall. This square was filled with people in colorful clothes. The windows were crowded with onlookers. People even lay on roofs or sat astride the wooden beams jutting from the walls beneath the roofs. The balconies were overflowing.

In front of the town-hall was a table covered with a green cloth with golden fringes and tassels. The magistrates sat at the table. They were dressed in satin robes embroidered with golden frogs and in sable hats with white feathers fluttering from shining buttons. At the head of the table sat the presiding official. . . .

On one side a Jewish girl stood fettered. Near her ten attendants held in check a wild horse. The presiding officer arose and, turning towards the audience, read from a paper the sentence pronounced upon the Jewish girl:

"This Jewess, offspring of Jewish parents, committed a great sin, a monstrous sin, which even all-merciful God could not forgive. She stole out of the ghetto on our recent holy day and walked about through our pure streets. She desecrated with her shameless eyes our sacred procession, our holy images, which we carried about our streets to the accompaniment of psalms and the beating of drums. With her accursed ears, she listened to the singing of our white-robed, innocent children and to the music of our holy drums.

"What certainty have we that the devil, the impure devil, who assumed the shape of this Jewish girl, the accursed rabbi's daughter, did not touch and desecrate one of our pure images? What could he want, the devil in this beautiful figure? For, I cannot deny that she is beautiful, as lovely as only the devil can make her. Just look at her insolently sparkling eyes beneath her modestly lowered lashes. Just look at that alabaster face, which long imprisonment paled but did not darken. Just look at her hands and the lean long fingers transparent in the sunlight. What did the devil want? Was it to tear ⧉ soul away from its devotion to the procession? Well, he succeeded. 'Look at this beautiful girl!' exclaimed one of our knights, a member of one of our finest families. This was too much for us to put up with. The armed attendants noticed her and seized her. The devil in her did not even resist. Why? Because our men were pure. They had just been absolved of all their sins and so the devil had no power over them. This, therefore, is the sentence pronounced by us upon the devil in the shape of this Jewish girl:

"She is to be tied by her hair, by her long devilish hair, to the tail of this wild horse. Let the horse gallop and drag her like a corpse over the streets which her feet stepped on in defiance of our holy laws. May her blood besprinkle our stones and wash off the impurity which her feet have brought to them!"

A wild shout of joy went up from all the throats round about the market-square. When the hysteria of wild shouts was over, the doomed girl was asked whether she had any last wish before her death.

"Yes," she replied, "I would like a few pins!"

"She must be out of her mind with terror!" muttered the magistrates.

"No!" she answered calmly and coldly, "this is my last wish and my only desire."

"Granted! And now, tie her!" commanded the presiding officer.

The armed attendants went over. Their hands trembled as they tied the black long braids of the rabbi's daughter to the tail of the wild horse, which could hardly be restrained much longer.

"Stand back!" shouted the officer to the crowd in the square. The people fell back and kept close to the walls of the houses. All raised their hands, in which they carried whips or rods or kerchiefs. All were ready to chase the wild horse. All breaths were bated, all faces glowed, all eyes blazed. In the excitement, nobody noticed that the doomed girl bent down quietly, pinned the edge of her dress to her feet, and stuck the pins deep, deep into her flesh, so that her body could not be uncovered when the horse dragged her through the streets.

This action was noticed only by the poor wandering soul.

"Let go!" commanded the presiding officer, and the attendants jumped aside. The horse darted forward and a shout arose from all throats. All whips and rods and kerchiefs went into action, whirling and whistling through the air. The terrified horse rushed past the market-square, past streets and by-ways, and far out beyond the town.

The wandering soul drew a blood-stained pin from the leg of the dying girl and flew to heaven.

"Just one more gift!" the angel at heaven's gate comforted the soul.

4 · THE THIRD GIFT

&3 The soul flew down again. It needed but one more gift.

Again seasons and years passed by and the soul once more sank into melancholy. It imagined that the world was becoming still smaller, with pettier people and pettier deeds, good and bad. It reflected:

"If God (praised be His name!) should ever want to stop the world in its course and bring it to judgment, if God were to place on one side an advocate who would pour out of a white bag rubble and specks of dust and on the other side an adversary who would pour out his bits and crumbs, a long, long time would elapse before the bags would be emptied—so much pettiness, so many little things.

"But, after the bags were emptied, what would the result show?

"The pointer would most certainly remain in the middle.

"With such trivialities, with so much pettiness, what was there that could make an appreciable difference in the weight?" What? Another feather, another straw, another grain of chaff, another speck of dust?

"What would God do with a world in such a condition? What decision would He arrive at?

"Would He decide to hurl the world back into void and emptiness? Of course not! The sins do not outweigh the good deeds.

"Would He decide to redeem the world? Most certainly not: the good deeds do not weigh more than the sins.

"Was it not more likely that He would say: 'Go on, fly between hell and paradise, love and hate, pitying tears and steaming blood, cradles and graves, ever on and on!' "

The soul was, however, destined to attain salvation. It is roused from its gloomy thoughts by the sound of drums.

Where? When?

It did not recognize either place or time.

It merely saw the courtyard of a prison. The rays of the sun playfully glided along the iron bars and the little windows and also reflected from the shining metal of the guns stacked up beside the wall. The soldiers were given whips, which they held in their hands.

Two long rows of soldiers were lined up, with a narrow passage in between. Someone was to be driven through the gauntlet.

Who?

A mere Jew of ordinary appearance, with a tattered shirt on his emaciated body and a skullcap on his half-shaven head. Now he was led over to the gauntlet.

Why this punishment? Who knows? This happened before our days. It might have been for theft or robbery or cruelty or perhaps even some trumped-up charge. It was, after all, before our age of progress.

The soldiers smiled and thought to themselves: why did they line up so many of us? Why, he wouldn't last halfway.

He was shoved over and pushed in to the passage between the lines. He started to walk. He went erect. He neither stumbled nor fell. He received lashes and he endured.

Fierce anger gripped the soldiers. He was still walking, still on his feet!

The whips whistled through the air like demons. They wound about the body like snakes. The blood of the emaciated body spurted unceasingly.

Hu-ha! Hu-ha!

He was half way through, when a soldier struck too high and off came the cap from the head of the victim. After a few paces, the doomed Jew noticed this. He stopped short, he hesitated, he reflected a moment, he made up his mind, and he turned around: he would not go with head uncovered. He retraced his steps to the spot where the cap had fallen. He bent down and picked it up. Then he continued on calmly, red and bloodstained but with the Jewish cap on his head. He walked erect until he collapsed.

And as he fell, the soul flew over and caught the cap, which had caused him so many extra lashes, and rushed with it up to heaven's gate.

The third gift was also accepted.

The saints interceded in behalf of the poor soul and the gates of paradise were opened for it after these three gifts.

The heavenly oracle said:

"Really beautiful gifts, gifts of extraordinary loveliness. They are of no practical use or material value, but their beauty is indeed rare."

From **Peretz,** translated and edited by Sol Liptzin, New York: Yiddish Scientific Institute—YIVO, 1947.

◄§ **MY NAME IS HAYIM by Moshe Prager** §► *A ringing story of faith by a well-known Yiddish-Hebrew writer: out of the Nazi horror and his own experiences in the death camps, he brings the story of Hayim, whose name means "life," and whose will to live was triumphant.*

◄§ Need I tell you who I am? How is it you did not recognize me? Why, everyone knew me at a glance. The hunters on every path, the pursuers on every road, the guards at every border— all of them, no matter what their uniform, black or brown, gray or yellow, many-colored or colorless, with all their outlandish insignia on sleeve and shoulder: crosses and stars, lions and eagles, and so on. They all recognized me—in summer as in winter, in rain and snow, at dawn or dusk. They scented me from afar. And can it be that you ask? Yes! I am a Jewish child! A Jewish child who climbs over every wall and fence, a Jewish child who mocks all his pursuers and persecutors. A Jewish child who fears not the Angel of Death himself. I am a Jewish child!

Where do I come from? Why have I fled? How did I escape? Why all these questions? You, too, want to cross-examine me? Very well, the secret can be told to you. I come from the pit of death, I climbed out of an open grave! It was there, in the grave, among the murdered ones, that I was born anew! That is why I am alive today.

What happened before has passed from my memory, and even if I should remember, I shall not tell you. I shall not tell of my little sister, of my two older brothers and the very littlest one, who was as lovely as a babe, and of my mother whom they carried off together with all the children except for me....I know naught!

I was born in that grave. I, too, was a corpse. I lay in the grave among all the Jews, with the children, oh! so many children. I, too, cried *"Shema Yisrael!"* (Hear, O Israel!), with all my strength I called upon the "Only One!" After that I died. Quietly I died and ceased crying out. But father held me in his arms all the time—on the way to the forest, and when he jumped into the ditch, and when we fell upon the bodies, and I had already died, he held me and pressed me to himself....And the pressure hurt so much. Then I forgot that I was already dead and began to scream. All was quiet, everyone in the ditch was quiet, and I cried out, "Papa!" And father held my hand and it hurt so badly. I wanted to free my hand, but he would not let go. I cried, but father did not answer; he had died. With all my might I called, but he did not awaken. He did not scream, but he moaned: "What is it?" And I asked: "Papa, have I died or am I alive?" And he answered quietly: "Oh, oh! you are alive, my child. Why do you cry? Are you in pain?"

Then I drew my hand from my father's arm and said: "No, nothing hurts me." And father whispered: "Be quiet, my child, all the Jews have died, and I am dying with them!" But I cried: "Father, I have not died. I live!" And father murmured: "Lie down, child, soon the pit will be covered with earth, and we shall lie among our people." But I cried: "Father, I am alive and I want to live! Come, let us flee from this place!" But he would not leave the pit of the dead; it was so hard for him to get out. Blood was streaming from him, and the blood was congealing me to him. I did not want to lie there any longer, and father said to me: "Get out of the ditch, my child. I am dying, but you are alive and have the will to live. Know, then, that out of the pit of death you are being born anew, and henceforth your name shall be—*Hayim* (life). Run quickly, Hayim, my son, and you shall live!"

What more can you ask? I have told all. I fled from the open grave toward the nearby woods, and the trees were my brothers and my friends. They let me climb up their trunks and hide among their boughs; the grass was my pillow; the plants, my daily bread. I told the forest the secret of my identity and my name. But the hunters lay in wait for me. They were in hordes and I was all alone; yet they all hunted me. Armed from head to foot, they were on guard day and night—in towns and villages, in the fields, on the roads and in the streets—all because of me. I realized that I bore a priceless treasure whose capture would warrant their ceaseless efforts. It was from these hunters that I learned how to protect this treasure.

Many a time when life became too heavy a burden, I thought of those Jews left in the pit, of father and mother and the children. I felt that I should not have left them, for it is not good for a Jewish child to live alone among the hunters. But each time when I saw them seeking another Jew I was once more convinced that a Jewish child is an invaluable treasure, and I swore that I would preserve it, come what might! At times they thought they had already caught the treasure: surrounding houses and streets, they climbed to the roofs and descended into the cellars searching high and low. They had an assorted array of instruments to detect every cry, moan and rustle in order to find my hideout. But I cherished the treasure, neither

weeping nor raising my voice. I held my breath, inwardly repeating my oath:

"My name is Hayim and I shall survive!"

Do not ask when the chase came to an end, for it never did
end. The faces and uniforms of the hunters merely changed. I
heard the war was over. The bells pealed—Victory! There was
singing on the streets: Down with the enemy! All men are free!
I wanted to come out into the street and cry: "I am a Jewish
child!" And so I fell into a trap. There were still the hunters
who spoke another tongue but were avid for the living Jewish
child. Yet again I had to keep my secret and stay under cover.
I escaped from the trap and smuggled across borders.

At the borders there were soldiers who like to play with
children, and their smiles almost lured me into another trap.
At first they would smile, and set me on their knees, offer me
candy and play with me. Soon they would begin to question
me: "Where are your mother and father, sonny?" But I remained silent and told them nothing. They persisted: "Where
do you live and why are you running away? And where do
you want to go, little boy?" I could no longer hold my tongue,
and I answered: "And where am I to live, please tell me, for
everywhere I am driven forth!" And I told them that in the
forest I had seen that each bird has its nest, each animal its
burrow, and each worm its shelter. I had hidden in ditches, in
cellars and in caves, and I had seen that each mouse had a
home. The mice, enraged that I had deprived them of their
lodging, would jump on me and bite me. But I did not know
where my refuge was. And still these hunters asked me where
I lived, and at last: "Are you a Jewish boy?" And their smiles
vanished. "What can it mean?" they asked. "Are Jewish chil-

dren still alive?" I laughed at all the guards and their borders:
"My name is Hayim, and from the pit of death I have arisen
to new life."

The chase continued, but the hunters could no longer de-
ceive me, Hayim. I recognized them from afar, and I have also
learned to know the Jew among thousands of Gentiles. . . .
Whether he tries to conceal his identity, to disguise himself
in all manner of ways, to speak any tongue on earth, I shall
know him nonetheless. It is useless to question me as to how
I can tell, for you would not understand in any event—one must
see it for oneself. It is so hard to explain. The Jew has a pair of
eyes: in one there is death; in the other—life. With one eye he
sees the corpses' pit, the river of blood and all that. And with
the other—no, I cannot convey it, for in both eyes there are
death and life; deep eyes that cry out, that pierce and flame and
throb. No, you would not understand it. Yet I cannot be deceived.

Suddenly I saw a man clothed in a beautiful new uniform, a
hunter like the others. I looked into his eyes and asked no
question. He, too, remained silent. I addressed him: "*Shema
Israel!* My name is Hayim!" Firmly he embraced me as had my
father on the way to the grave and drew me close in his arms,
as father had in the grave. But this time I felt no pain, nor did
I cry out. Before I said a word he had understood all. Then he
said: "What a beautiful name. Every Jewish survivor should add
it to his own. You shall live together with all living Jews. You
must know that the Jews have a land of life, which mothers
every motherless Jewish child. In that land, the mother of all
Jews, you, too, shall live!"

Do not ask me how he brought me here. I know how to keep

a secret and *that* secret I shall not reveal, for I am not a child any longer. Though he carried me close to him over land and sea, I did not cry. At first the sea was gentle, but after a while it grew angry, ranting and raving so that I thought that the sea, like the grave, would swallow the Jews. Yet I did not cry. Day and night it raged without abating. I answered only:

"My name is Hayim, and I shall live!"

And the sea made its peace with me, singing a lullaby as mother had sung when she soothed and rocked our beautiful "little one" to sleep. The sea cradled me to sleep, and I, who am not a child, fell asleep like a little boy....

I shall tell no more. And suddenly *he* awakened me calling: "Hayim! Hayim!" He carried me on his back, but he was submerged in the water except for his head and arms. My feet, too, were wet, but I did not cry. A few more steps and he was out on sand—nothing but clean sand. He fell upon this sand, threw me upon the sand and lay there weeping like a little child. He said to me: "Hayim, Hayim, here you shall live with all Jews —for *Am Yisrael Hai.*" He took a handful of sand and played with it like a little boy and I lay there in the sand, and it was warm and dry and soft, and the sand caressed me like a mother, and I, too, began to weep. Just this once. Never again shall I cry, as surely as I live and my name is Hayim. I shall only laugh, be joyous, sing and say:

"My name is Hayim, I want to live! I shall live in spite of our enemies, the tormentors and hunters!"

On the day of the Hunger Strike,
13th of Nisan, 5706

This story, translated by Helen Atkin, appeared in the **Pioneer Woman,** June 1946.

V

ON TORAH

Once a man came to Shammai and said: I will accept
Judaism if you will teach me the Torah while I stand
on one leg.

Angry, Shammai ordered him to depart.

Then the man went to Hillel. And he became a
Jew. For Hillel accepted his challenge, and spoke thus
to him: "Do not do unto others what you would not
have done unto yourself. This is Torah: the rest is
commentary."

Adapted from the Aggadah

◆§ **THE GUARANTORS** ◦► *A simple parable from the Aggadah, the commentary on the Holy Scriptures, carries a deep message of the Jewish tradition: that Torah means education and knowledge, and that through each new generation, through the children of the Jewish people, will this way of life be preserved.*

◆§ It is told, in one of the ancient books, of the time when God was ready to give the Torah to the children of Israel.

As Israel stood ready to receive this precious gift, the Holy One, Blessed be He, said: "I will give you My Torah. But first you must bring Me good guarantors, that I may know you will guard it well."

And the children of Israel said: "Let our fathers be our guarantors: Abraham, Isaac, and Jacob."

And God said: "Your fathers are not acceptable to Me. Abraham is unacceptable, Isaac is unacceptable, and Jacob is unacceptable. But offer Me good guarantors, and I shall yet give the Torah to you."

Then the children of Israel said: "Master of the Universe, we offer you our prophets as guarantors."

And God replied: "The prophets are unacceptable to Me. Bring Me good guarantors that I may give the Torah to you."

And then the children of Israel said: "Let our children and our children's children be our guarantors."

And the Holy One, Blessed be He, said: "Your children and your children's children are good guarantors. For their sake will I give the Torah to you."

Adapted from the Aggadah by A. E.

⤳ A PSALM OF DAVID ⤶ The Book of Psalms 19: 8-12.
The Psalms are often called the poetry of all peoples. They are lyrical poems of universal appeal; they center about one theme —God. In magnificent language, they reveal human hopes, meditations, thanksgiving, and prayer. Here is the poetic expression of one man's feeling about God's Law.

The law of the Lord is perfect, restoring the soul;
The testimony of the Lord is sure, making wise the simple.
The precepts of the Lord are right, rejoicing the heart;
The commandment of the Lord is pure, enlightening the eyes.
The fear of the Lord is clean, enduring for ever.
The ordinances of the Lord are true, they are righteous
    altogether;
More to be desired are they than gold, yea, than much fine gold;
Sweeter also than honey and the honeycomb.
Moreover by them is Thy servant warned;
In keeping of them there is great reward.

⋖§ **THE ORDINATION** by **Harry Sackler** §⋗ *The stead-fastness of the Jewish people in their devotion to Torah, keeping them alive through every period of persecution and martyrdom, is shown in this historical incident from a novel by a well-known American Hebrew and English writer. It happened in Palestine, about 140 C.E. The Roman Emperor Hadrian placed the edict of death upon any Jew found in the study of Torah or the observance of any religious ceremony. Rabbis like Akiba and Hanina ben Tradion gave their lives rather than submit. Old Judah ben Baba had secretly trained seven disciples, and the time came to ordain them as rabbis and teachers in Israel. A secluded ravine was selected as the site for the ceremony, and a potter was put on guard so that no other lives would be endangered by this forbidden act. . . .*

⋖§ In the afternoon of the appointed day, they started for the ravine. The seven disciples went there singly, after having been told how to reach the spot where they were to meet. Rabbi Judah, unequal to covering the distance on foot, was provided with a donkey, which Enoch led over the rutty and rubble-strewn track.

While Enoch kept his eyes wide open for anything indicative of danger, Rabbi Judah sat strangely silent, his feeble frame swaying and jerking with the quick and uneven motion of the little beast. He felt sad and forlorn. The ordinations he remembered were all bright and joyful events, not only for the young scholars who had attained the "crown of learning" but also for the masses of the people, who would come to witness the ceremony and honor their future leaders. The crowd would appear in festive garb. The candidates for ordination would wear new garments of white with ornamental strips at the hem of their mantles. After the investiture of each scholar, the people would shout joyously and sing his praises. This time there will be no one to do it, except the scholars themselves—and that pious potter who was walking silently alongside of him.

"And there will be no rejoicing," reflected Rabbi Judah bitterly. "How can one rejoice when the whip of Edom lacerates the back of the righteous? It is hard to grow elated over the advent of new teachers, when the old ones are forbidden to teach and when the performance of the commandments entails stripes and torture and, not infrequently, death. The ways of God were indeed inscrutable. One rides to ordain teachers secretly—at the risk of many precious lives—at a time when all Jewish law is banned and all Jewish teaching proscribed. If the Lord of the World was pleased to give the victory to His detractors, then why demand of His own—?"

But here the old man shook himself and placed his hand on Enoch's shoulder as if seeking refuge in the unquestioning faith of his companion.

They descended the steep side of the ravine and, down below, they found the seven waiting for them at the appointed place. This was a small clearing near an overhanging ledge that shielded them completely against prying eyes from the track above. Beneath the ledge there was an opening, a sort of natural shaft, which, slanting downward, led to another hollow, covered with brushwood. Enoch pointed out the shaft to them and jestingly remarked that the quickest way to reach the other side was to crawl through snake-fashion. Somehow he also came to mention the fact that in the adjoining hollow there were several small caves, fit for a night's shelter.

Rabbi Judah raised his weak eyes toward Enoch. He was about to ask him whether he was apprehensive of some imminent danger. But one look at Enoch told him the story. He knew that he must bestir himself.

"Beloved sons," began Rabbi Judah, trying to speak evenly, "I am about to confer upon you the authority which you have long deserved to receive. It was merely my tardiness and excessive caution that delayed it so long. Akiba, of blessed memory, found but few flaws either in your piety or in your learning and it is really his mandate that I am carrying out today. If the great master were only one with us now—" He fell silent for a moment and swallowed hard once or twice before he resumed. "Now, need I tell you that the beginning of all wisdom is the fear of God? You know it. Or need I caution you not to make your learning a spade to dig with? You know that as well. Therefore, as your superior—not in wisdom but in years—I am now going to confer upon you the right to be teachers and judges in Israel and may the spark that I strike now, in the isolation of this ravine, become a pillar of fire that will lead Israel from the gloom of these distressing times to the glory of a brighter day."

"Amen," said the seven and Enoch with them.

Now Rabbi Judah cast a rapid glance over the seven. After a moment of hesitation, he walked quickly towards Meir, laid his hands upon the head of the disciple and exclaimed, "Henceforth, Rabbi Meir, you may teach and you may judge. May your light brighten the world."

"Ordain for us men like these—not foolish, stupid, unscholarly fellows!" sang out the others. It was one of the customary responses at an ordination and they made an effort to cheer the old master by conjuring up the spirit and the jollity of the holiday.

"Rabbi Simeon!" called Rabbi Judah, while laying his hands on Simeon's head. "Henceforth you may teach and you may judge. God will hear you and Israel will follow in your footsteps."

"He is both wise and modest," sang out the others. "He is of noble lineage and blessed with riches. May his like increase in Israel."

"Rabbi Judah ben Ilai," called Rabbi Judah and proceeded to invest the third of the disciples.

But as he was doing so, Enoch had detached himself from the group, clambered hurriedly up the side of the ledge and, stretching himself flat on his stomach, began peering towards the track above from the shelter of a rock. The others understood and they lowered their voices as they intoned the response, all the while casting anxious eyes upon the potter and his movements, midway on the ledge.

"Proceed, Rabbi Judah," said Enoch, whispering. "But please lower your voice."

Jose ben Halafta, Johanan of Alexandria, Eleazar ben Jacob and Nehemiah were soon ordained and Rabbi Judah's face wreathed itself in smiles.

"It is done," he said, as if addressing someone who was invisibly hovering near the scene. "But we shall omit the public discourse, which is the custom at the occasion, as the time is not propitious."

Even while Rabbi Judah spoke, a ripple of voices floated

down to them from the track above. Enoch put his hand over his mouth as a signal for silence. They stood still, their eyes glued to the face of the potter. They wondered whether he had already caught a glimpse of those above. Were they merely stray wayfarers? Or were they Roman soldiers, sent by Junius Gargarus after them? There was no fear on the potter's face. Only his eyes had narrowed into two small slits, like that of an animal at bay watching intently the movements of its assailant. The hum of voices above began dying down—was rising again —and stopped. Now Enoch raised his head slightly. He smiled. Obviously the danger of being detected was over. And suddenly he lowered his head quickly, alarmingly. Because just then the little donkey brayed.

"Quick now!" he whispered, as he slid down from the ledge, motioning that they leave the clearing and seek shelter beneath the rock.

"Spies?" asked Simeon breathlessly.

"No," said Enoch hoarsely. "The spies must have seen us before, when we came down here. Now it is soldiers."

"How many are they?" asked Simeon.

"Too many to be driven off with stones," replied Enoch. "But we may yet escape, if we get to the caves in the hollow before they come down here. They may never discover the opening beneath the ledge. Come, Rabbi Judah, let me help you crawl through first."

"No, Enoch," replied Rabbi Judah, warding off the approaching potter with outstretched arms. "No! The younger ones must go and you must go with them. You always wanted to finish this good deed. Now, do so."

"This is not possible," said Simeon, who suspected that Rabbi Judah intended to remain behind and so cover up their flight. "We shall carry you in our arms."

"I am too old to be carried in arms," said Rabbi Judah firmly. "Go now, my children. I wish it so."

"If we do that," said Meir, "we shall be scorned and derided by all the generations to come. They left their master to the mercy of the Romans, they will say of us. Force us not to disobey you, master."

"If you persist, you will destroy what I built," said the old man sternly. "I am not thinking of you now. This may cause you pain and even bring shame upon you. Still, do as I bid you."

They surrounded him and their eyes pleaded with him to relent. Simeon spoke again: "Oh, master, how can we leave you? How can we go and leave you?"

"You are but leaving a rock that no one should ever care to roll over," he said softly. But when he read in their eyes that they were nevertheless determined to stay and perish with him if need be, he became stern again. "Am I no longer your master?" he asked, raising a threatening forefinger. "I command you to go. Leave me at once!"

Simeon and Enoch were the last ones to go. But Rabbi Judah took Simeon's hand, forced him to lie down and crawl through the shaft into the hollow. Then as Enoch followed, he bent down and said: "Potter, this is the seed that God saved from the blight and the destruction. Remember!"

"I know," said Enoch, his voice choking with tears.

"Potter," he heard the old man's voice through the shaft, "I promise you that wherever I shall sit in the World to Come, you shall sit at my right side." But when Enoch turned around for a last glimpse of Rabbi Judah on top of the shaft, he found that the light was shut out from the upper end of the opening. It was stuffed up with the mantle of the lone, old man.

Enoch joined the others. He found them standing with bowed heads—shamefaced, perplexed, unable and unwilling to leave the spot.

"Come now," said Enoch. "I know what he wants me to do and he promised me a great reward for doing it. The seven must not fail."

They followed him through the pathless brush. They walked cautiously, treading lightly, lest one careless step betray their presence to the approaching enemy. Though their walk lasted but a few minutes, it was an arduous and tiring task. Now and then, one of them would halt, as if desiring to retrace his steps back to the ledge, where Rabbi Judah was even now standing alone, alone—. But finally they reached the caves, while the sun was bending low towards Usha.

"He is alone there to meet the enemy," said Simeon to Meir, as they entered one of the caves.

"Aye," said Meir musingly. "Rabbi Judah ben Baba, racked by a bad cough, eighty years old and for many years without sleep, subsisting on a few drops of goat's milk, is sallying forth alone to meet Rome. The God of Israel should be pleased with him."

When the moon rose over the ravine, Enoch and the seven ventured out of their hiding-place. Enoch was the first to crawl through the opening. Several moments he stood in the shelter of the rock and was listening carefully. A jackal howled in the distance. Nothing stirred.

The others followed. Fifty paces from the ledge they discovered the body of Rabbi Judah. It had been riddled with darts. Only the face remained uninjured and there was a smile on the set lips, as if he had died perfectly content with his lot.

"He had always envied Akiba his martyrdom," said Meir.

"So he did," agreed Simeon, as he spread the old black mantle over the blood-drenched corpse. "Now we shall carry him back to Usha and bury him before the sun rises."

"This you will leave to me, Rabbi Simeon," said Enoch. "None of you must tarry here any longer. This path, there, will bring you to Shefar'am before the third watch is over."

Tenderly he raised the body and placed it across his right shoulder. "You may follow the funeral to the edge of the ravine," he said as he started to go.

They did. Then they watched him struggle up the steep incline and march off westward, while the moon was shedding a tinge of silver on the potter and his burden. When he disappeared, they turned eastward, towards Shefar'am.

From the novel by Harry Sackler: **Festival at Meron**, New York: Covici-Friede, 1935.

◦§ **TORAH THE BEST MERCHANDISE** ੩◦ *What pos-*
session can never be stolen or lost, but remains with its owner
forever? Here is a story from the Ma'aseh Book, a group of
medieval legends told originally in Judaeo-German, or early
Yiddish, and based on Midrashic lore. The Midrash is a body
of literature interpreting and developing the meanings of the
Biblical text, relating Jewish tradition to everyday life, and
serving as a deep source of idealism for our day.

◦§ Once upon a time a ship carrying merchants and merchandise sailed over the sea, and among the passengers was a great
scholar. The merchants began to converse about the wares
which they carried with them, and what they intended to buy.
Finally they asked the scholar what merchandise he had, and
he answered: "I carry all my goods with me." The merchants
searched the whole ship for his wares, for they thought that he
had precious stones, but they could find nothing. So they jeered
at him and said that he had no merchandise at all. The scholar
replied: "Why are you laughing at me? The goods which I carry
are of greater value than any which you have in the ship's
hold."

As they continued traveling on the high seas, they were
attacked by pirates, who robbed them of all the merchandise
which they had in the ship. When they landed, they found
themselves quite poor and had nothing to eat or drink or any
clothes to put on. The scholar, however, went into the town
and entered the *bet hamidrash*. When the people heard what an

important man he was, they at once brought him clothes and gave him a large amount of money. Moreover, the good people of the town followed him out of the city.

When the merchants saw the great honor which was shown to the Jew, they begged his pardon for having laughed at him, and asked him to request the townspeople to give them something to eat so that they might not die of hunger, for he had seen that they had been robbed of their property. And the scholar replied: "Did I not tell you that my merchandise was more valuable than yours? For you have lost your property, but mine is still with me. Furthermore, one who buys and sells does not always gain; sometimes he gains and sometimes he loses, and even when he gains he is not sure that the profit will remain with him, but the Torah remains forever, in this world and in the next. I was right, therefore, about the goods which I had with me."

From **The Ma'aseh Book**, Vol. I, by Moses Gaster, Philadelphia: Jewish Publication Society of America, 1934.

◆§ THE LEGEND OF THE HONEY by Jacob Benlazar ℥
During the Middle Ages, and for many years thereafter, the Jews of Europe showed their love for learning and Torah in an unusual custom. In it they expressed their wish to pass on to their children this same love. Here is a legend about this custom.

◆§ There once lived a man named Simon ben Yehuda. If one were to look at Simon, and then look at his neighbors, one would say: here is one like all the others, and the others are like him. For Simon seemed to be an ordinary, industrious man who led a simple life.

But, as it is said, you cannot know a man unless you look into his heart. And it was only the angels in heaven who knew the pureness and greatness of Simon's heart. For Simon gave to the poor without hope of reward from God or his fellow man. He forgave his enemies and bore no hatred. He was modest and carried his goodness deep within himself.

One day, high in heaven, a group of angels met and decided that Simon's goodness should be rewarded. For seven days and seven nights they talked. What could they do for Simon? He had a wife whom he loved dearly, and a son precious beyond measure to both of them. Simon was happy. But at last an idea came to the angels. What better reward for Simon than to have a son who would be a seer and sage among his people? Then the angels sent messengers across the wide world to gather together the purest honey from the best bees, bees who had fed on none but the loveliest flowers in the world's gardens.

When Simon's son reached the proper age, his father brought him to school for the first time. As the boy sat in front of his books, a strange sweet smell came to him. He touched a book, and put his finger to his mouth, and then he tasted the most wonderful sweetness he had ever known. For the messenger of the angels had covered the pages with the rare honey they had gathered.

So Simon's son learned to love the book that was set before him. And as the angels knew, from this love there grew a love for learning, and a great hunger to know all that was known by man. So began his days of study, days that led to honor and fame as a seer and sage among his people.

This is the story that is told, and this is why the custom arose of dabbing honey on the pages of a child's first book.

⊸§ **THE TWO BROTHERS by M. Ben-Eliezer** &⊷ *There were two brothers, worlds apart as people, but as one in their love for Torah. A Hebrew writer of the late nineteenth century portrays the Old World in a sentimental and affectionate way.*

⊸§ In our town there were many groups, organizations, and study circles. But the *Hevrah Shas*, the fellowship which studied the Talmud daily, was the most honored of all. Those who belonged to it were the intellectual aristocracy. All who sought to leave behind their daily toil would gather after the Morning Service at the southern wall in the old synagogue, and experience true spiritual joy.

In my time, the leader of the *Hevrah Shas* was Rabbi Nehemiah.

Rabbi Nehemiah was blessed with two "crowns": the crown of learning, and the crown of wealth. When one saw him during business hours in the market place, where he owned a big hardware store, one could not believe that this husky, aggressive merchant was a great scholar. But when one saw him in synagogue, wrapped in a long *tallit* with *tefillin* on forehead and arm, studying the open Gemara, one could not imagine that this studious, pious scholar had any earthly cares at all.

Nehemiah had a younger brother named Akiba. It was said that Akiba was even more learned than Nehemiah, but, unlike his older brother, he was a poor man. However, he was always cheerful and always content with his lot.

No two people could have been more different than these brothers. While Nehemiah was stern, strict, removed from peo-

ple, Akiba was of a sweet disposition, loving people and enjoying their company. The poor especially would come to him for
advice and guidance. He listened to all their troubles with kindness and patience, and gave generously of comfort, advice, and
help.

Because they were so different, the townsmen called the
older brother "Shammai," and the younger, "Hillel."

Of course, Akiba too was a member of the *Shas* fellowship.
Often he would gently chide his older brother for snobbishness,
for not associating with anyone outside his special group.
Nehemiah, on the other hand, often rebuked his brother for
hobnobbing with the poor, the "tailors and cobblers," as he
called them.

In those days the number who studied Talmud daily began
to dwindle. The older generation was passing and the young
did not take its place....

One day the workers of the town, the "tailors and cobblers,"
decided to organize a Study Fellowship of their own, to study
Haye Adam daily. They asked Akiba to be their leader.

When the news reached Nehemiah, he confronted his
brother: "It is not proper for you to do this."

Whereupon Akiba answered him gently: "The Torah was
given to all Israel."

Nehemiah's reply was immediate and stern: "Akiba, you will
have to account for this. You are opening a new door...lower-
ing standards. In the past, Jews sacrificed time and strength to
learn....A Jew who could not pass the test gave honor to one
who acquired learning with blood and sweat....There were
standards then....Now, everyone can boast of 'scholarship'....

Every tailor and cobbler will become a Rabbi....The loss will be greater than the gain."

The argument grew more and more heated as Nehemiah's anger swelled. He realized at last that Akiba would not give in, and he burst out:

"If you persist in doing this, I won't have anything more to do with you!"

From that day the brothers were separated. They did not visit each other, nor talk to one another. When Akiba's daughter was married, Nehemiah did not appear at the wedding. He sent a wedding gift through his wife, and people thought he did not want to mingle with the "tailors and cobblers" whom Akiba had invited.

II

Akiba's study group grew in numbers and popularity, as Nehemiah's dwindled. And Akiba's influence among the people grew. When he taught, crowds came to hear him. When the month of Elul came, Akiba would preach repentance to his people. Passers-by were amazed and moved to see Akiba's students listen in rapt attention, tears flowing from their eyes.

Akiba watched over his people like a shepherd. And they responded with love and reverence. Especially did they show their affection for their leader on Simhat Torah. Then they would all gather at his home, and carry him to the synagogue with song and hymn. They embraced him, and kissed the hem of his garments.

When Nehemiah saw all this, he remarked disdainfully: "Idol worship!"

One day the news spread: Akiba was ill. The doctor reported

that his condition was critical. Akiba's people did everything possible for their beloved Rabbi....They recited Psalms three times a day. Each one offered up private prayers. They made pilgrimages to the graves of saints, and implored their souls to intercede on behalf of their Rabbi. But Akiba grew worse.

A day before Akiba passed away, Nehemiah went to visit his brother. When the haughty, hard Nehemiah saw Akiba on his deathbed, he wept like a child. Akiba opened his eyes, recognized his brother. He wanted to raise his hand to greet him, but couldn't.

Nehemiah came closer and asked gently: "How are you feeling?"

Akiba did not answer. After a long pause, he said weakly: "Nehemiah..."

The brother bent over him and heard Akiba whisper: "I am near death."

"While life remains, hope in God's mercy!"

"My end is near," the sick man said. "Who will take care of them? Orphans....With whom shall I leave them?"

Nehemiah forced the tears back: "I'll take care of your family! You need not worry!"

"I don't mean *them*. Nehemiah, I have one request to make of you."

"Anything I can do, I will do."

"I want your promise. Give me your hand on it."

Nehemiah gave him his hand.

"Nehemiah, after I die ... *you* take my place and teach them 'Haye Adam'."

Nehemiah hesitated. He hadn't expected such a request....

But his brother's eyes were on him.

"Will you?"

Nehemiah nodded his head.

When the week of mourning ended, Nehemiah took his brother's seat at the table of the *Haye Adam* Study Fellowship. As he took his brother's book in hand, his face softened, his voice lost its harsh tone. Indeed, he looked and spoke just as Akiba. And even more strange, when the lesson ended he had become the Nehemiah of old.

Thus he continued, until his dying day. . . .

From **Olam Over (A Passing World)**, by M. Ben-Eliezer, Tel Aviv: Meir, 1928. Translated by A. E.

◄§ **THREE WHO ATE by David Frishman** §► *What is the essential meaning of Torah? Not a series of prohibitions but an affirmation: life must be lived. David Frishman (1860-1922) famous Hebrew writer, critic, poet, wrote an immortal story on this theme, modeling his hero after Rabbi Israel Salanter.*

◄§ Even if I live many many years and my days are as numerous as the sand, I shall not forget that day and what happened. Forever shall the memory of the men who took part in it live in my mind. For they were not ordinary men, but giants.

Those were trying times such as had not been experienced before or after. Like a bolt from the clear sky, cholera descended upon the land. From distant parts of the East the Angel of Death swooped down over our little town. It struck young and old without pity. Not a home was untouched. In broad daylight and in the stealth of night it killed. Those who were still alive hovered helplessly between life and death....Especially hard hit was the Jewish part of the town. There was not a family, not a house, without its toll of many dead.

Summer was coming to an end and the solemn season approached. Then came the most solemn of all days—Yom Kippur. *That's* the day I shall remember as long as I live.

It is the eve of the great fast—the Day of Atonement—the most solemn hour . . . *Kol Nidre.*

At the Reader's Desk in front of the Ark stands not the *hazan* and two trustees as usual, but the Rabbi and his two assistants. Around them burn memorial candles which sputter and wave.

At the wall stand the worshipers wrapped in prayer shawls, their heads covered with white skull caps. Their white cloaks are caught up by white girdles. Shadows in sharp outline on the wall sway and pray with them. Entranced, the congregation looks at these shadows. Are they the shadows of the living, or of the dead who have come back to join us in worship on this sacred night? Hush! The voice of the Rabbi is heard, echoed by the voices of his assistants:

"By the authority of the Heavenly Tribunal and of the Court below, with the Divine Sanction and the sanction of this holy congregation, we declare it lawful to pray together with those who have transgressed."

I sit up tense. Why recite these words? Tonight of all nights? Where are the sinners with whom we are permitted to pray? Isn't he afraid to give an opening to the Angel of Death in this hour of awful calamity?

A great fear envelops me. It is as if it shrouds all the people, young and old.

I see the Rabbi ascending the pulpit. Will he preach *now*? Will he lecture to them *now* at a time when the dead lie before us?

But the Rabbi neither preaches nor lectures. He recites the Memorial Service for the dead. He reads the list of those who died in the last few days. What a long and terrifying list! Will it go on forever? Will it never end?

Suddenly I think it might be better if he called off the names of those still living. They are far fewer in number.

That night and that Service I shall never forget. It was not prayer, really, but a long, long, agonized groan springing from the depths of the heart and piercing the sky until it reached to the highest heaven. Never have people offered up their souls with greater anguish. Never have more bitter tears been shed by human eye.

No one left *Shul* that night. The worshipers remained to recite hymns and psalms; then they stayed on to study the Mishnah and mystic works.

I, too, stayed in *Shul* that night. As I recited, my eyes closed and in my dream I saw angels, ascending and descending. And among them, lo, I saw the Angel of Death, his body covered with blinking eyes.

In the early morning two men were found, dead. They lay wrapped in *tallith* and white robe as if they had been made ready for burial. Messages came steadily from the outside; frightening, tragic messages. But no one wanted to hear them lest he learn the worst. . . .

The night was a terrible night. But the day that followed was worse.

Even now I need but close my eyes to see the entire scene. I am transported back among the people in the *Shul*. . . . Now it is the afternoon of Yom Kippur.

The Rabbi stands on the pulpit, erect, tall. His face is bathed in a halo of light. All eyes are on his noble figure. My own cannot leave his face. The Rabbi is seventy, perhaps eighty years old. But he is straight and tall and he towers above his congregation. His beard is as white as silver. But whiter sevenfold is his hair, thick and long and shining. His face glows with a pale light; his lips are bloodless. Only his eyes are bright, big and dark and flashing with a youthful fire.

(From early childhood, I learned to revere our Rabbi. I knew that he was a man of God, respected everywhere as an authority in Jewish Law. I knew too that he was inclined to be lenient in his interpretations of the Law, and that no one dared oppose his decisions.)

The Musaf Service had ended and the congregation stood mute and spellbound. No one breathed.

And the Rabbi begins to speak. At first his voice is thin and weak. But as he continues, it becomes clear and resonant. Soon it thunders above the audience. He speaks of the holiness of Yom Kippur, of atonement and repentance, of the living and the dead, of the great plague that is destroying without mercy and without end. For how long, O Lord? For how long?

As the Rabbi speaks, his cheeks grow flushed and color returns to his lips. I hear him say: "When man suffers, he should examine himself. Not only should he give an accounting to himself about those things that concern his soul, but those that concern his body, his health, his flesh, as well."

I trembled as these words entered my mind, for suddenly I understood. I understood what they meant.

He goes on to speak of the importance of personal hygiene and cleanliness. He describes how dirt and contamination lead to pestilence and death, how in these awful days death seizes those weakened by hunger and thirst....

Now he seems to be gathering his strength for a climax. "The Torah says, 'And they shall live [by My commandments] and not die.' There are times when the commandments of the Torah may be disregarded, so that human beings may live. Life comes before Torah."

Fear possesses me. Suddenly I hear someone weeping, and my heart is torn to pieces; I, too, begin to cry.

To this day as I shut my eyes the scene that follows lives

before me. The Rabbi calls his two assistants to him. Hurriedly they ascend the platform and approach him, one to the right, the other to the left. They whisper together. But why do his cheeks flame while theirs turn white as chalk?

My ears hear familiar words, yet strange.

The people utter a heart-rending groan which cuts through the synagogue and hangs suspended above the congregation. Again I hear: "With the sanction of the Divine and with the sanction of this Holy Congregation, we declare it lawful to eat and drink today."

A deathly silence. No one moves; no one breathes.

I hear my heart beat: one, one-two. A great dread descends upon me. I look at the wall and again I see the shadows of yesterday's dead, and the day before, and the day before that.

He is asking Jews to eat on Yom Kippur! Because of the pestilence—because of the pestilence—because of the pestilence. I break into a loud weeping. The whole congregation weeps. On the pulpit the three weep; yes, even the great Rabbi weeps as a child would cry.

He stands there, imploring in his soft, gentle voice. Tears swallow his words. But again we hear him say:

"Eat! We must live, not die. This is the time to disregard the Law. The hour demands it." But no one moves.

The Rabbi declares that the responsibility will be his. His people are innocent; they shall not be punished.

Suddenly his voice changes. No longer does he plead. He commands. The words come from his mouth like speeding arrows.

But the people do not move.

Like a hurt child, he pleads again.

"Why do you disobey me? What do you want of me? Why do you torment me so? Think you that this decision came easily to me? I have struggled with myself from dawn."

His two assistants also take up the plea.

Now his face becomes white; his head falls to his breast. A groan passes from one end of the *Shul* to the other, and then a murmuring.

"It is the will of God," he speaks quietly, almost to himself. "I am eighty years old today. Never have I broken a commandment. But this is also the Law; it is the commandment; it is God's will. *Shamash!*"

The *Shamash* hurries over and the Rabbi speaks to him. Then he turns to his two assistants and speaks to them. They nod their heads in agreement. The *Shamash* returns and he carries a tray of wine, glasses, and cookies.

And although I shall live many years and my days will be long, I shall never forget that scene. Even now as I shut my eyes I see it as if the whole thing lived before me: three who eat; three great sages in Israel standing on the pulpit on Yom Kippur, and eating before the eyes of Israel.

Who knows the inner struggle they waged before they reached this terrible decision? Who can fathom the suffering and anguish they experienced in their souls?

"I have set the example," said the old Rabbi in a steady firm voice. "Blessed be the name of God."

Many in the *Shul* eat and swallow their tears with their food. And as I recall these things a warm flood of light pours out of me and envelops this room, this table, and this paper on which I record these childhood memories of the three who ate.

Translated by A. E.

THE DEMOCRACY OF TORAH by Milton Konvitz

The Torah was set down more than 2000 years ago. What has given it such life and vitality over the centuries? A Cornell University professor writes of the essential democracy of the Jewish tradition, where all men are equal before God.

Three Crowns were recognized by the Jewish people: the crown of the Torah, the crown of the priesthood, and the crown of the kingdom.

Aaron was worthy of the crown of the priesthood and obtained it. David was worthy of the crown of the kingdom and obtained it. The crown of the Torah remains, so that no man shall have the pretext to say: "If the crown of the priesthood and the crown of the kingdom were yet available, I would have proved myself worthy of them and have obtained them." For the crown of the Torah is available for all. For God says: "Of him who proves himself worthy of that crown, I reckon it to him as if all the three were yet available, and he had proved himself worthy of them all. And of everyone who does not prove himself worthy of the crown of the Torah, I reckon it unto him as if all three crowns were yet available, and he had proved himself worthy of none of them."

The crown of the Torah is not inherited; it was worn by men who earned their living by cobbling shoes, weaving flax, or making candles. Ben Azzai said: "If any man humiliates himself for the Torah, eats dry dates and wears dirty clothes, and sits and keeps guard at the doors of the wise, every passer-by thinks him a fool, but at the end you will find that all the Torah

is within him:" and if the Torah is within him, he may wear
the crown of the Torah. A famous passage in *Pirke Abot* is the
following:

"This is the way that is becoming for the study of the Torah;
a morsel of bread with salt thou must eat, and water by measure thou must drink, thou must sleep upon the ground, and
live a life of trouble, the while thou toilest in the Torah. If
thou doest thus, 'Happy shalt thou be and it shall be well with
thee;' happy shalt thou be in this world, and it shall be well
with thee in the world to come. Seek not greatness for thyself,
and crave not honor more than is due to thy learning; and
desire not the table of kings, for thy table is greater than theirs,
and thy crown greater than theirs; and faithful is He, the Master
of thy work, to pay thee the reward of thy labor."

As water is priceless, said the Rabbis, so is the Torah priceless; and as water is free for all, so is the Torah free for all. But
the Torah was also compared to wine: as wine cannot keep in
vessels of gold and silver, but only in cheap earthenware vessels, so the words of the Torah are preserved only in him who
makes himself lowly. "The greater the man," says the Midrash,
"the humbler he is." Man, especially one who wears the crown
of the Torah, must be as humble as is God Himself; wherever
you find the greatness of God, there, too, you will find His
humbleness. For "God loves nothing better than humility,"
said Rabbi Johanan: "The words of the Torah abide only with
him who regards himself as nothing." The Torah was not to be
used as an ornament with which one might adorn himself; nor
was it to be used as a spade with which to dig; knowledge of
the Torah was its own reward; it is only to study the Torah

that God created man: study of the Torah is his purpose, his end, his happiness, and his reward. "Do the words of the Torah for the doing's sake; speak of them for their own sake. Do not say: 'I will learn Torah so that I may be called wise, or sit in the College, or gain long days in the world to come!' " Nor may one charge fees for the teaching of the Torah; for the words of the Torah are free; God gave the Torah free: "He who takes a fee for the Torah destroys the world."

The humility with which the greatest of the three crowns was to be worn is illustrated by the following incident related in the Talmud:

"One day, at the close of the fig harvest, Rabbi Tarfon was walking in a garden, and he ate some figs which had been left behind. The custodian of the garden came up, caught him, and began to beat him unmercifully. Then Rabbi Tarfon called out and said who he was, whereupon they let him go. Yet all his days did he grieve, saying, "Woe is me, for I have used the crown of the Torah for my own profit." For the teaching ran: "A man must not say, I will study so as to be called a wise man, or rabbi, or an elder, or to have a seat in the College; but he must study from love. The honor will come of itself."

From The Jews, Vol. III, edited by Louis Finkelstein, Philadelphia: Jewish Publication Society of America, 1949.

VI

ON ISRAEL

When the Lord brought back those that returned to
   Zion,
We were like unto them that dream.
Then was our mouth filled with laughter,
And our tongue with singing;
Then said they among the nations:
"The Lord hath done great things with these."
The Lord hath done great things with us;
We are rejoiced.

Psalm 126:1-3

ᴥ JACOB BECOMES ISRAEL ᴥ Genesis 32:25-32 ᴥ

One of the famous passages in the Bible: at night on a river bank, Jacob struggles with an angel. Jacob is victorious, and out of his victory comes greater strength, and a new name for himself and his people—Israel. It has been said that this passage represents the fight each person, and each nation, must wage with itself: against evil, and for goodness and justice.

ᴥ And Jacob was left alone; and there wrestled a man with him until the breaking of the day. And when he saw that he prevailed not against him, he touched the hollow of his thigh; and the hollow of Jacob's thigh was strained, as he wrestled with him. And he said:

"Let me go, for the day breaketh."

And he said: "I will not let thee go, except thou bless me."

And he said unto him: "What is thy name?"

And he said: "Jacob."

And he said: "Thy name shall be called no more Jacob, but Israel; for thou hast striven with God and with men, and hast prevailed."

And Jacob asked him, and said: "Tell me, I pray thee, thy name."

And he said: "Wherefore is it that thou dost ask after my name?"

And he blessed him there.

And Jacob called the name of the place Peniel: "for I have seen God face to face, and my life is preserved."

And the sun rose upon him as he passed over Peniel, and he limped upon his thigh.

⋖§ THE VALLEY OF DRY BONES ⋗ Ezekiel 37:1-14 ⋖§

The Bible gives us a magnificent prophecy—and a lesson of hope for all time. When it seemed that the world itself was at its very end, life came forth. . . .

⋖§ The hand of the Lord was upon me, and the Lord carried me out in a spirit, and set me down in the midst of the valley, and it was full of bones; and He caused me to pass by them round about, and, behold, there were very many in the open valley; and, lo, they were very dry.

And He said unto me: "Son of man, can these bones live?"

And I answered: "O Lord God, Thou knowest."

Then He said unto me: "Prophesy over these bones, and say unto them: 'O ye dry bones, hear the word of the Lord: Thus saith the Lord God unto these bones: "Behold, I will cause breath to enter into you, and ye shall live. And I will lay sinews upon you, and will bring up flesh upon you, and cover you with skin, and put breath in you, and ye shall live; and ye shall know that I am the Lord." ' "

So I prophesied as I was commanded; and as I prophesied, there was a noise, and behold a commotion, and the bones came together, bone to its bone. And I beheld, and, lo, there were sinews upon them, and flesh came up, and skin covered them above; but there was no breath in them.

Then said He unto me: "Prophesy unto the breath, prophesy, son of man, and say to the breath: Thus saith the Lord God: 'Come from the four winds, O breath, and breathe upon these slain, that they may live.' "

So I prophesied as He commanded me, and the breath came into them, and they lived, and stood up upon their feet, an exceeding great host.

Then He said unto me:

"Son of man, these bones are the whole house of Israel; behold, they say: 'Our bones are dried up, and our hope is lost; we are clean cut off.' Therefore prophesy, and say unto them: "Thus saith the Lord God: Behold, I will open your graves, and cause you to come up out of your graves, O My people; and I will bring you into the land of Israel. And ye shall know that I am the Lord, when I have opened your graves, and caused you to come up out of your graves, O My people. And I will put My spirit in you, and ye shall live, and I will place you in your own land; and ye shall know that I the Lord have spoken, and performed it, saith the Lord."

◄§ RACHEL WEEPS FOR HER CHILDREN ?► *Legends like these, part of Midrashic lore, were handed down from father to son. Even the sing-song of the dialogue was so preserved through the ages. ...*

◄§ Our mother Rachel came forward before the Holy One,
   blessed be He, and said:
"Master of the universe, it is clearly known to you
how your servant Jacob loved me with an exceeding love,
and worked seven years for my father for me,
and when he had completed those seven years,
and the time came for my marriage to my husband,
my father took counsel, and gave my sister to my husband in
   my stead.
And it was a very hard thing for me to bear,
yet I had compassion on my sister,
lest she go forth to shame,
and I acted with charity toward her,
and was not jealous of her.
And if I, who am flesh and blood, dust and ashes,
was not jealous of my rival,
and did not send her forth to shame and disgrace,
You, O King, living, enduring, and compassionate,
why are you jealous of idols which are nothing real,
and have exiled my children,
so that they were killed by the sword,
and the foe did with them as they wished?"

At once the compassion of the Holy One, blessed be He, was
   aroused, and he said:
"For your sake, Rachel, I shall return Israel to their place."
Therefore it is written:
"Thus saith the Lord:
A voice is heard in Ramah, lamentation, and bitter weeping,
Rachel weeping for her children;
she refuseth to be comforted for her children, because
   they are not"
And it is written:
"Thus saith the Lord:
Refrain thy voice from weeping, and thine eyes from tears; for
   thy work shall be rewarded."
And it is written:
"And there is hope for thy future
And thy children shall return to their own border."

From **Hammer on the Rock,** edited by Nahum N. Glatzer, New York:
Schocken Books, 1948.

⊷§ **EPISTLE TO THE JEWS IN YEMEN** by Moses **Maimonides** ⊷§ *The Golden Age of Spain was rapidly coming to an end in 1172 C.E. under the fanatic Mohammedan rule. The Jews in North Africa and Spain were given the choice of conversion to Islam, or death. It was then that a new star appeared on the Jewish horizon—Moses Ben Maimon. Of him it was said that from Moses to Moses, there was none like Moses. His famous* Letter *to his suffering people was a gift of courage and healing.*

⊷§ The antagonism of the nations toward us is due to our unique position as a people of faith. This is why their kings oppress us, to visit upon us hatred and hostility. But the Creator endowed us with confidence, so that whenever persecution or fury against Israel arises, it will surely be endured. The power of the kings presses down upon us and they exercise a hard rule over us; they persecute and torment us with oppressive decrees, but they cannot destroy us or wipe out our name.

Do you know, brethren, that in the time of the wicked Nebuchadnezzar, Israel was forced to worship foreign gods, and only Daniel, Hananiah, Mishael, and Azariah were rescued? But in the end, this king and his authority were destroyed and truth was restored. The same happened in the time of the Second Temple, when the wicked dynasty of Seleucus came into power and persecuted Israel in order to destroy its religion. The Syrians forced Israel to desecrate the Sabbath and the covenant of circumcision and publicly to renounce belief in God. This oppression lasted fifty-two years, and then God annihilated both the government and the religion of the enemy.

God promised us through his prophets that we shall never perish and that we shall never cease to be a nation of faith. Our life is correlated with the existence of the Lord. As it is said: "For I the Lord change not, therefore ye, O sons of Jacob, are not consumed." And Moses, our teacher, said in the Torah: "And yet for all that, when they are in the land of their enemies, I will not reject them, neither will I abhor them, to destroy them and to break My covenant with them; for I am the Lord their God."

Therefore, brethren, be strong and of good courage. If persecutions arise, let them not disconcert you. Let not the mighty hand of the enemy and the weakness of our nation frighten you. These events are but trial and proof of your faith and your love. By holding firm to the law of truth in times like these, you prove that you belong to those of Jacob's seed who fear God and who are named "the remnant whom the Lord shall call."

It is your duty, our brethren of Israel, who are scattered over the whole earth, to strengthen one another. The older should encourage the younger, and the prominent men the multitude. The nation should be united in the name of truth, which does not change. Raise your voices in strong faith, proclaiming to all that God is One, that Moses is His prophet and the greatest of all the prophets, that the Torah is the word of the Creator. Keep ever in mind the event on Mount Sinai.

My brethren, rear your children to understand that great

event; expound to every group and community its significance.
The event on Mount Sinai is the pivot on which our faith turns,
the foundation that leads us to the truth. Understand, my
brethren, the meaning of that covenant: the nation as a whole
witnessed the word of God and His presence. This event should
strengthen our faith and enable us to resist the strain of persecutions and intolerance in times like these. It is said: "God is
come to prove you, and that His fear may be before you, that
ye sin not." This is to say, that experience should give you
strength to withstand all trials to which we may be subjected
in times to come. Therefore, brethren, hold fast to the covenant
and be steadfast in your faith.

From **In Time and Eternity,** edited by Nahum N. Glatzer, New York:
Schocken Books, 1946.

◄§ WHAT IS A JEW? by Leo Tolstoy ৪► *What is a Jew?* *One of the world's great writers, the Russian novelist and Christian-philosopher, gives his answer to the age-old question.*

◄§ What is a Jew? This question is not at all so odd as it seems. Let us see what kind of peculiar creature the Jew is, which all the rulers and all nations have together and separately abused and molested, oppressed and persecuted, trampled and butchered, burned and hanged—and in spite of all this is yet alive? What is a Jew, who has never allowed himself to be led astray by all the earthly possessions which his oppressors and persecutors constantly offered him in order that he should change his faith and forsake his own Jewish religion?

The Jew is that sacred being who has brought down from heaven the everlasting fire, and has lighted with it the entire world. He is the religious source, spring, and fountain out of which all the rest of the peoples have drawn their beliefs and their religions.

The Jew is the pioneer of liberty. Even in those olden days, when the people were divided into but two distinct classes, slaves and masters—even so long ago had the law of Moses prohibited the practice of keeping a person in bondage for more than six years.

The Jew is the pioneer of civilization. Ignorance was condemned in olden Palestine more even than it is today in civilized Europe. Moreover, in those wild and barbarous days, when neither life nor the death of anyone counted for anything at all,

Rabbi Akiba did not refrain from expressing himself openly against capital punishment, a practice which is recognized today as a highly civilized way of punishment.

The Jew is the emblem of civil and religious toleration. "Love the stranger and the sojourner," Moses commands, "because you have been strangers in the land of Egypt." And this was said in those remote and savage times when the principal ambition of the races and nations consisted in crushing and enslaving one another. As concerns religious toleration, the Jewish faith is not only far from the missionary spirit of converting people of other denominations, but on the contrary the Talmud commands the Rabbis to inform and explain to everyone who willingly comes to accept the Jewish religion, all the difficulties involved in its acceptance, and to point out to the would-be proselyte that the righteous of all nations have a share in immortality. Of such a lofty and ideal religious toleration not even the moralists of our present day can boast.

The Jew is the emblem of eternity. He whom neither slaughter nor torture of thousands of years could destroy, he whom neither fire nor sword nor inquisition was able to wipe off from the face of the earth, he who was the first to produce the oracle of God, he who has been for so long the guardian of prophecy, and who transmitted it to the rest of the world—such a nation cannot be destroyed. The Jew is everlasting as is eternity itself.

This is a portion of a letter published in **Der Israelit**, Frankfort on the Main; it appears in **Stars and Sand**, edited by Joseph L. Baron, Philadelphia: Jewish Publication Society of America, 1943.

◄§ **THE MESSENGER FROM THE HOLY LAND by S. Y. Agnon** ◈▸ *One of the leading Hebrew writers of today, living in Israel, weaves into this tale the ancient question of Diaspora: what is the life of the Jews to be in lands other than the homeland? The story begins when a stranger from Jerusalem visits a city in Poland. He finds the town deserted, quiet: the Jews are all gathered in the synagogue, in deep and long lamentation. His curiosity aroused, he seizes one of the elders and says he will not let him go until he learns the meaning of this strange mourning. The elder begins his tale. . . .*

◄§ "Know, then, that in days of yore this city was renowned for study and wisdom, and indeed it deserved its reputation, for all its inhabitants were learned in holy lore.... In the large *Beth Midrash* learned scholars would sit with their Talmud folios in their hands; all through the city it was almost impossible to hear one another talk for the din of those at study. And after they had finished the evening prayer, all the householders and students would gather together, each with a candle in his hand until the light of their candles outshone the moon. And on this regard they took great pride in their city and would say, 'This city is the very crown of beauty. There is none like it in all the world.' And there is another story about one of the residents of our city who was visiting in another city, when the time came for the sanctification of the new moon. Turning aside in contempt, and turning up his nose, he exclaimed, 'And is this what you call a moon? Truly, there is no moon to equal the moon of our city!'

"Thus many years passed. The people were prosperous and

the houses filled with the Torah. But the charity box of Rabbi
Meir, the miracle worker, remained empty. It became covered
with a spider web as thick as a silver dollar, and filled with
golden rust. But they were not hard-hearted people, who turned
their backs on charity. God forbid! They merely said, 'Our land
is Eretz Yisrael and our city is Jerusalem, but before we dis-
tribute money to the poor of knowledge in *Eretz Yisrael* whence
not even one worthwhile book comes to us, we might better
build for ourselves a great *Beth Ha-Midrash* where we shall
reap glory for ourselves through worthwhile books.' And so
they did. . . . The workmen toiled from early morning till late
at night. And if they tried to rest and refresh themselves, the
elders of the city would strike them with the long stems of
their pipes and say to them: 'O, you ignoramuses! The Torah
wanders about without a roof and you dare make saloons for
yourselves.' And they brought tables as strong as iron, which
could stand up without breaking under the great pile of books
that the men while studying would place upon it. And when
they dedicated the *Beth Midrash*, they began to expound on
the glory of such a lodging place for the Torah. But what could
they say? Were it not for the Rabbis, may their memory be
blessed, who said that he who has not seen the Holy Temple
before its destruction has never seen a truly beautiful building,
then they might have considered their building truly beautiful,
—as it was, they had to remain quiet.

"When that *Beth Midrash* stood complete in all its glory
there chanced to come to the city a certain *Meshullah*, or col-
lector of alms for Palestine. He brought his belongings to the
Beth Midrash and walked about aimlessly. But as they were all
deeply engrossed in their studies, no one greeted him, no one

met him with a *Borukh Haba*, nor did anyone ask him whence
he came or whither he was going, whether his lodging was provided for, or with what wealthy man he was staying. They did
not set any food before him nor did they give him anything
warm to drink. The *Meshullah* fetched out of his bag two or
three dates and a piece of bread a little bigger than a date, and
though his meager repast did not fill his stomach, his sighs filled
his soul to overflowing. He drank some water from the basin,
took his staff and went to the Rabbi to get permission from
him to speak in the *Beth Ha-Midrash* that Sabbath. The Rabbi
told him that the city was full of Torah and all the inhabitants
learned in holy lore, and that when a preacher came to the city
they would worst him in legal discussion until he no longer
had any courage to speak, and that in the end he would have
to descend from the pulpit disappointed and shamefaced. The
Meshullah, however, did not heed the warning of the Rabbi but
answered him in the words of the Biblical verse, 'For the sake
of Zion I shall not be silent.' So he returned to the *Beth Midrash*
and then printed signs announcing that a learned man who was
a fine speaker had come to town from the Holy City of Jerusalem, etc., and that the occasion would be a rare treat for the
audience. He went out into the street, entered a bakery shop
where he bought a pot full of paste and then went about the
city sticking up his signs.

"That Sabbath the entire town came to the synagogue. This
learned man mounted the pulpit, wrapped himself in his prayer
shawl, and standing near the holy ark, began to expound the
praises of *Eretz Yisrael* and the qualities of the holy land, and
the love of Jerusalem, may it be rebuilt and re-established. And
he wove a fine argument about the settlement of *Eretz Yisrael*,

delivering it quietly and without excessive zeal, and it was all seasoned in the most approved manner with the spices of the Torah. . . . While he was yet expounding a voice was heard from the congregation. The *Meshullah* turned his head and listened while someone asked thus and so about his words. He answered him thus and so. The questioner countered and answered him, not so, but thus and so. The *Meshullah* brought forth proof from the Talmud, thus and so. They told him, however, that he had not gone deep enough into the matter to fill the hole of a needle, and that if it came to a decision, it was thus and so. And they broke down his arguments and they rebutted his contentions until his face was gloomily dark as the bottom of a pit. . . . He stopped in the middle, touched his lips to the curtain of the Ark and burying his face in the Shield of David, cried until the threads glistened from his tears like pure gold, and then taking off his *tallith*, shamefacedly descended from the pulpit. He went to the back of the room and there behind the oven tearfully paced back and forth. . . . So the Sabbath passed and the *Meshullah* found himself without funds to continue his travels, for all the money which he had previously collected he had already sent ahead to *Eretz Yisrael*, confident that the sons of Israel, 'the merciful ones, the sons of merciful ones,' would not be tight-fisted, Heaven forbid. And so when they finished the morning prayer, the *Meshullah* approached one man after another on the subject of making some contribution for *Eretz Yisrael*. But here this one cried and there that one cried, and though all of them gave plenty of excuses, no one gave any money. . . .

"The *Meshullah* realized that nothing was to be obtained from them, so he took his staff and bag, went up to the holy ark, and burying his head among the holy scrolls, cried bitterly, 'Ribono shel Olam—Dost thou not know that not for my own glory did I do this, nor for the glory of the house of my father, but for the poor of Thy people, Israel, who dwell in Thy presence in Thy holy land and suffer the pangs of hunger? How many pilgrimages and hardships I have gone through! The waves of the sea have risen up against me to drown me in the deep, and robbers have sought to take my life. Yet not even once have I said to thee, "Why hast thou troubled me?" And now I have come to Thy sons who are learned in Thy holy law, and see what has befallen me!' And immediately he closed the holy ark, touched his lips to the curtain, went to the door, kissed the Mezuzah and began to sing in a wonderful voice, the words of the Rabbis of Blessed Memory. 'The Lord loveth the gates which are distinguished in the study of the Law,' and he continued, 'and all the synagogues and houses of study which are outside of the Holy Land are destined to be transplanted to Eretz Yisrael.'

"At that moment all felt the earth tremble underneath their feet. They fled for their lives and stood watching from afar. They saw the walls of the Beth Midrash bend toward the east like a man who is about to walk. And the Meshullah walked before the Beth Ha-Midrash singing in a sad voice, 'The Lord loveth the gates which are distinguished in the study of the Law,' and he himself responded, 'and all the synagogues and houses of study which are outside of the Holy Land are destined to be transplanted to Eretz Yisrael.' He had not yet finished, when the Beth Midrash was moving after him, books and tables and all. The Meshullah walked slowly and the place where the Beth Midrash had stood was now bare and naked, hiding itself in the evening shadows.

"When the residents of the city saw this, they all began to sob and to weep and awoke to complete repentance. And they decreed for themselves and for their offspring, until the coming of the redemption—may it come speedily in our days, Amen—that they should observe, every year, a strict fast on that day. And the day of this fast we spend in penitence and supplication. And we give a great deal of charity to the poor of the Holy Land and we go to the river and pray that we may be pardoned for not having bestowed upon the *Meshullah* honor that was his due. And we fast until long after midnight when we partake of a light meal in order that we may not perish, God forbid, from the great stress of our grief and penitence. And thus we fulfill the three-fold function of fasting and prayer and charity, true penitence in body, in voice and in deed."

Immediately I tried to comfort them and said, "My teachers and masters, I testify by heaven and earth, that I have seen a *Beth Midrash* such as you have described, in Jerusalem. There the building stands on a holy site and the sons of Israel, the holy ones, study in it the holiness of our holy Law. And," I continued, "Rejoice O Israel, that even the houses in which you study the Torah, the Holy One blessed be He, brings to *Eretz Yisrael*, and if the Holy One, blessed be He, troubles Himself about those things which are but beams and stones and brings them to *Eretz Yisrael*, how much more is it likely that with Israel itself, who studies the Torah and the Commandments, He will do likewise. It is indeed as has been said, 'Even them will I bring to My holy mountain and make them joyful in My house of prayer.' May it be thy will. Amen."

From the **Brandeis Avukah Annual,** edited by Joseph S. Shubow, 1932; translation by Harold I. Saperstein.

HARVEST IN THE DESERT by Maurice Samuel ❧ *A distinguished American author takes us to the early pioneering days in Israel, before it became a state, and in this story of an amateur astronomer, helps us see its people, their comradeship, and their spirit.*

❧ I went out of the theater, along streets thronged with Tel Avivians, among crowds of gay young people, past cafés jammed with customers. The movie houses and meeting halls were emptying. At the corner of Allenby Street and the sea-front I ran into an American journalist, fresh from the west, and we walked to and fro along the beach while the crowds dwindled and the lights in Jaffa across the bay were extinguished one by one. In a pause of the conversation I happened to stop and look up at the sky, which was, as always between the rainy seasons, marvelously clear. I noticed then that an astronomical event, of minor significance but of great beauty, was in preparation. The gibbous and brilliant moon was close to Spica, a star of the first magnitude in the constellation of Virgo. The whole sky was revolving, against the diurnal motion of the earth, to the right; but the moon, in her slower motion about the earth, was crawling leftward through the constellations. The illumined half of the moon pointed right, toward the long-vanished sun; the unillumined and invisible half, or rather less than half, pointed left. Some time that night an occultation would take place; that is to say, the invisible bulk of the moon would blot out, at a given instant, and with startling instantaneous effect, the star Spica. Now that, as every amateur astronomer will attest, is something to be seen, especially through a telescope.

I explained all this to my friend, and told him that I had a telescope at home; and if I only knew what time the occultation would take place, I would treat him to the celestial spectacle at my expense. Very much at my expense, since only one of us could have his eye glued to the telescope at the climactic moment. Such are the enthusiasms of Zionists and amateur astronomers. But how was I to know when the occultation would take place? And where, in God's name, was I to find out? Now if this were only New York, I would surely be able to ring up someone with a Nautical Almanac. And failing that, there was always some newspaper information service. But we were in Tel Aviv, a great city no doubt, but after all. . . .

My friend said: "The other day, walking through the *Shechunat ha-Po'alim* (the Workers' Quarter at the seaward end of the Rothschild Boulevard) I saw a telescope mounted on a roof. If you're so set on the occultation, let's go there. The owner of the telescope may know."

"At this hour of the night?" I answered, dubiously.

"If he's as hipped on the subject as you are, he'll be up right enough."

So we set out along the Yarkon Street, parallel with the beach, and came to the Workers' Quarter. There, sure enough, on the flat roof of one of the single-storied houses, a telescope was mounted on a tripod. No one was standing beside it, but a light was shining in one of the windows below.

"*Vive* Tel Aviv!" I exclaimed. But the best was yet to come.

We knocked timidly at the door, and a woman came out. I asked whether the *ba-al ha-bayit*, the householder, her husband, was the owner of the telescope. But he was a night-worker, and was away till morning.

What a pity! I was about to apologize and withdraw, when the woman said:

"Before he went out, an hour ago, he left a message with me. He said: 'It may be, though it is not at all likely—and still one can't tell—it may be, and one must always be prepared, that someone will come to the house because there's a telescope on the roof, and ask you what time a certain event will take place.' —she looked closely at the paper in the light streaming out from the kitchen—"it will take place at eleven seconds and fifty-three minutes after one o'clock. If anyone wanted to use the telescope at that time, he was welcome to it."

When I was able to catch my breath, I thanked her. No, we did not want to use the telescope. I had one at home. I only wanted the information. I asked her also to convey our thanks to her husband—to Adon—"Hillel," she said.

But by now the excitement of the occultation had been displaced in me by another excitement.

"The absurdity of it!" I said, exultantly, as we walked back. "The utter delicious and heartening absurdity of it! That's what makes a homeland. Not just land, agriculture, funds, factories, experts, administrators and blueprints, but cranks, mystics, vegetarians, bibliophiles, poets—amateur astronomers who remember that someone might want to know the minute and split second of an occultation. A thing like this couldn't have happened in Uganda [a proposed homeland]."

"No, it couldn't," said my astonished friend. "Why should it?"

from **Harvest in the Desert**, by Maurice Samuel, Philadelphia: Jewish Publication Society of America, 1944

◆§ **THE HEROISM OF THE JEWISH BRIGADE by Pierre van Paassen** ⧽ *An American minister, known for his many books and journalistic writings, tells of a heroic chapter in the history of the Jewish Brigade, during World War II. The African campaign was raging, and a unit of Jewish engineers was engaged in laying down a minefield at Mechili. After a German bombing attack, the British promised anti-aircraft guns and reinforcements. The orders were to finish laying the mines and hold the field at all costs. The promised help never arrived.*

◆§ In three days' time Mechili was surrounded on three sides by a ring of enemy tanks, both German and Italian, and the engineering garrison was cut off from all contact with the outside world. Before attacking, the German brigadier in charge of operations sent a tank with a white flag and the message to hoist the signal of surrender. That happened on the morning of June 10. Major Liebman said to the German officer who brought the message: "We have no white flag! All we have is the banner. This we are going to fly. It's the blue flag of Zion! . . ."

"*Sie sind Jude*" (You are a Jew), said the German in surprise, clicked his heels, saluted, and walked off.

Six hours later the tanks came rumbling towards the position, sixty in one column and twenty-five each in two others. A flock of Stukas which appeared simultaneously was forced to drop its bombs prematurely when it was attacked by British Kittyhawks. But the tanks rumbled on. The Jews held their fire until the first metal monsters reached the barbed wire stakes. Then they let go. Two tanks blew up when they struck mines.

nineteen were hit by anti-tank fire. One Jewish sergeant alone accounted for seven of them.

Meeting with so much unexpected resistance, the main tank column, which belonged to the Italian Ariete Division, halted, signaled to the others, and started to withdraw. This was the moment for which Major Liebman had prepared. Sixty of his men who had been hidden in dugouts near the extremities of the mine field rushed out when the Italians turned tail and bombarded the retreating tanks in their vulnerable rear. . . . Some of the Jews jumped on the back of the tanks, firing their revolvers into the lookout slits and gun holes. In this way five more enemy machines were accounted for. As the last Italian caterpillars moved off British fliers swooped low over the mine field and waved their hands at the Jews.

The following day the Germans subjected Mechili to a merciless aerial bombardment. They repeated the assault twice a day. For seven days the bombs rained down, turning the mine field into a wailing hell of steel in which it did not seem possible for human nerves or human life itself to endure. One squadron of Stukas had not passed over and dumped its ghastly load before the next one winged into sight. They dive-bombed the trucks, the dugouts, the guncrew. They churned and plowed up the mine field, filled it with craters two stories deep until Mechili was an inferno of boiling red-hot iron missiles in an inferno of blistering desert heat. Still the Jews held out.

On June 20 the tanks returned en masse. Upon their approach the weary, hungry defenders clambered out of their foxholes and manned the guns. Again they repelled the assault of the Ariete Division while an aerial battle went on above their heads and British fighters drove off the Stukas that came to administer the *coup de grâce* to the garrison. But at the end of that day, although forty-one smoking tanks testified to the deadly accuracy of the Jewish gunners, only ninety men were left out of Major Liebman's original five hundred.

Ten more days passed. Each day the Italians renewed the attack, raking the mine field with a murderous fire, getting nearer and nearer to the central position with each onslaught. Then the water well was hit and stove in by a well-placed Stuka bomb, and the agony commenced. From that day on the men were reduced to a daily pint of water from the tin cans dropped by the R.A.F.

Major Liebman had banded his men closely together around the deep, central dugout. Here they were going to make their last stand. Outside lay the bodies of their comrades which the Stukas would not leave buried but plowed up and sent up in the air in a ghastly, maddening dance of rotting flesh and bones. Two men went out of their minds on June 25, two more the next day. Three men rushed off shrieking into the desert. The bombardment continued. With the summer heat mounting every day and the scorching wind blowing up clouds of dust, the men's thirst grew unbearable. Some drank gasoline and perished. Others drank their own urine and went mad with the pangs of greater thirst afterwards. Nobody spoke a word those last days. Rifles grew burning hot in the men's hands.

Forty-five men were left on July 1, a handful of unrecognizable scarecrows, scarcely human in appearance, unkempt, haggard, covered with grime, emaciated, some stark naked, having had the clothes blown off by the concussion of five-hundred-pound bombs exploding near by.

On July 2, they faced their last assault at six in the morning, lost two more men, and put the Italians to flight once more. At ten o'clock, a lookout man, who could scarcely speak, his tongue cleaving to the roof of his parched mouth, warned Major Liebman that a column of trucks was approaching, led by an automobile bearing the tricolor of France. The commander, although wounded in the head and in the groin, staggered to his feet and waved the answering signal.

The French troopers approached. They were the remnant of the Free French from Bir Hacheim who had received orders to withdraw the night before. The Jews stumbled into the open, looking like so many tortured ghosts. General Koenig of the Free French walked up to Major Liebman and embraced him. "*Vous avez tenu bon, jusqu'au bout*" (you held out till the end), he said. Then tears choked the Frenchman's voice.

The Jews were given water, and the Major informed them that they were to accompany the French column. The siege was over. French soldiers were loading the remaining equipment on trucks. A flock of Spitfires sailed by, the pilots waving. . . .

One Jewish soldier took down the blue and white flag of Zion, rolled it up, and was about to place it in its holder when General Koenig saw him and asked him a question.

"We are not permitted to fly that flag," explained Major Liebman. "It's against regulations . . ."

"Pardon," said General Koenig, "I am in command here. *Je m'en fous pas mal des regulations*. I don't care a damn about regulations. . . . That flag goes on my car in front, next to the tricolor. That's where it belongs. *Nous sommes victorieux, tous les deux*. We have both come through victoriously!" And turning to his men, the French officer shouted: "*Legionnaires! Le drapeau juif! Salut!*" Legionnaires! The Jewish flag! Salute!

From **The Forgotten Ally**, by Pierre van Paassen, New York: Dial Press, 1943.

✺§ THE THREE-FOLD COVENANT by Yehuda Yaari ৪৵

*A contemporary Israeli writer, one of the early pioneers, tells
a moving story of modern-day Israel, the meaning of the Covenant, and the return of the sons of Israel to their people.*

✺§ My neighbor is an immigrant from Germany who came to
Palestine some time ago among the other refugees from race-
hatred and persecution. It was just at that time that we came to
live in our new flat in one of Jerusalem's modern suburbs. He
lives on the lower floor, and I on the one above.

We have no personal acquaintance with each other. It has
always been rather hard for me to get to know my neighbors.
Several times a day I pass the door of his flat, and the name en-
graved in outstanding Hebrew letters on a brightly polished
brass plate gleams at me from the door as though it were alive,
proclaiming "Richard Oppenheimer."

Sometimes my neighbor and I meet in the hall in the mornings when I am starting out for work and he, too, is going off
about his business. The moment he sees me he raises his hat in
my direction and uncovers his flaming red hair, smiles at me
and says:

"*Shalom. Guten Morgen.*"

And the echo of his thick, trumpeting voice fills the entire
entrance hall.

"*Shalom.*" I return his greeting, raising my hat as well in
politeness.

Apart from these infrequent morning meetings and our
polite greetings, there is no contact between us. Were it not

for the aroma of his pot-bellied cigars ascending to me every now and then through his open window I would not know that he was there at all. He is a peaceful sort with quiet ways, and his home is just as quiet. There are no noisy children; nor does as much as the hoarse voice of a phonograph or radio disturb us. If anything, it is he who must be aware of the presence of his neighbor. Not that I have either phonograph or radio or even noisy children in my flat; but I live above him and there can be no scrape of a shifted table or movement of a chair or even noisy tread in my flat which does not sound in the flat below like a clap of thunder.

Turning over the paper one morning, I noticed that, as is the custom here, somebody had sent congratulations to Richard Oppenheimer through the columns of the paper on the birth of a son. Which Richard Oppenheimer could be meant? My neighbor? Yes, my neighbor and none other. The person offering congratulations was H. Levy and I knew H. Levy to be my neighbor's business partner, for on their big shop for the sale of pharmaceutical products and cosmetics in the main street the name "Oppenheimer and Levy" was written up large for all to see. I read through the congratulation once, twice, and yet a third time, and pondered upon the mysterious ways of our lives. In the very house in which I was living a woman had lain writhing in birth pangs and I had known nothing of it; a son had been born to my neighbor; and although no more than the thickness of a ceiling separated us, I had become aware of the fact only through the pages of a newspaper. Through my brain passed a sudden vision of the woman taken with the first pains, of the bewildered husband taking her to the hospital.

My thoughts went directly on to other things, I forgot my neighbor and the son that had been born to him, and began to consider my daily work.

I forgot my neighbor; but that evening I remembered him again. I had just sat down to eat supper when there was a knock at the door. I opened it and in came my neighbor, Mr. Richard Oppenheimer.

"*Shalom. Guten Abend.*"

I invited him in. He stood silent and nervous for a few moments with a narrow forehead, his bronze eyes squinted slightly, his red lips looked as though they were swollen, his body was well-set and soldierly, and the back of his neck, I noticed, was fleshy and scarred. In my Polish birthplace they used to call such a countenance an Esau face. I could see that he found it hard to express himself. So I came to his aid.

"Please sit down, Mr. Oppenheimer; can I do anything for you?"

"Thanks. Yes, yes," he stammered and this time his voice was gentle and restrained, entirely different from the voice that sometimes used to trumpet a greeting at me in the hall below. "Yes, yes; I have a request to make of you. . . . The Circumcision will take place tomorrow—I suppose you know that my wife has had a son. . . ."

"Yes, I heard about it, Mr. Oppenheimer. Congratulations." I shook his hand, and it immediately became easier for him to speak.

"I'll tell you quite frankly. I don't know what has to be done. I'm in a fix. I don't know how to say the blessing tomorrow at the ceremony . . ." His reddish face grew still more flushed and something childlike and innocent about him touched me to the heart; for nothing is so touching as a strong face suddenly softening.

I took my prayer-book from the bookcase and opened it to the Circumcision Service.

"Here you are," said I.

"Hm, hm," he cleared his throat and half-smiled in still greater confusion. "But what's to be done? I don't know how to read Hebrew . . . Not so much as a single letter. Maybe you'd be good enough to write down the blessing for me in Latin characters." In his nervousness he began fiddling with his fingers.

I was nonplused. There was something astonishing and even startling in this confession of helplessness on the part of a man like my neighbor. He always went about with such firmness and self-assurance. His morning greeting said: I know everything. I can achieve everything; and now this confession of helplessness, of inability to read the prayer-book. I suddenly felt sorry for him and strove to overcome my astonishment. Sitting down, I wrote out the blessing in Latin characters as he had requested, in block capitals so that he would be able to read it easily. Then I read it out to him three or four times. He in turn repeated it after me in Hebrew with a weird German accent. . . . When he began to grow a little familiar with the blessing I rose, thinking it was finished. I offered him my hand but he did not take it.

"I have yet another request of you; pardon me, for giving you so much trouble," he stammered in a gentle voice. "Another slight request. The name, sir. We find it hard to choose a name for him. You know that my name's Richard. But for our

son we want a nice Hebrew name, something out of the Bible
. . . Please, do you think you could find us a nice name from the
Bible?"

I took the Bible off my table and opened it at random to
Numbers. The first words my eyes struck were "Elizur, son of
Shedeur."

"Elizur," I read from the book.

"Elizur, Elizur." My neighbor was as happy as though he had
found a valuable treasure. "Elizur. Wonderful. *Grossartig.* A
wonderful Biblical name. Thank you, sir, thank you. Elizur!"
He gave me his hand to take his leave and simultaneously invited me to come to the Circumcision. It was a social invitation,
made to do his duty, it seemed to me. Nonetheless I decided to
be present, for I felt that I had a share in the festivity. I had
taught him the blessing and I had found him the name; how
could I do other than participate in the celebration?

It was a summer evening, hot, dry, and still. I sat on my
balcony to breathe a little fresh air. My neighbor sat below me
on his balcony. For a long time I heard him murmuring to himself as though he were praying, repeating the blessing, "to mage
our zons ender indo de Govenand off Abraham our Fader." For
the first time I was aware that we were neighbors.

The following morning I put on my Sabbath suit, took some
time off from work and went to the hospital which my neighbor had mentioned to me the day before, in order to be present
at the induction of his son into the Covenant of Abraham. I arrived there a bit late, after my neighbor had already said the
blessing. I made my way through the crowd till I reached the

Seat of Elijah. The circumcised mite was yelling at the first pain he had suffered in his life, and Reb Shlomo Jacob, the circumciser, who is said to have inducted a full myriad of Israelites into the Covenant of our Father Abraham, stood bandaging the child.

Richard Oppenheimer was swathed in a new silk *tallis* and stood leaning against the godfather's chair. His face was set and strained and pale. I felt sorry that when he had entered my flat the evening before I had thought to myself that he had an Esau face. No, the face was now no longer that of an Esau; he now seemed to be a man overwhelmed by something fateful which could not be avoided. There was a tremendous difference to be seen in his face, and I observed it with wonder. When they reached the naming of the child his face brightened up a little. "Elizur, son of Richard," he proudly told the circumciser. The latter automatically corrected it to "son of Reuven." My neighbor was perplexed for a moment; then his glance met mine. He smiled at me.

It did not take long for the entire ceremony to be completed and the yelling baby to be taken to its mother. The assembly sat down at the tables to enjoy the wine and sweetmeats. They were a noisy lot, congratulating and toasting one another, chattering, rattling their glasses and laughing. Most of them were German immigrants, of whom I hardly knew one. I sat myself down by the oldest of them all, who had been godfather. Both the expression on his face and the fact of his having been godfather attracted me. His white hair rose like a silver diadem on his head. His trim beard and mustache marked his face as though with a capital T. He had the face of a respected man, a man of standing. Had I begun addressing him as *"Herr Hofrat"* he would assuredly have responded; his face told me as much. But since I was not certain, I contented myself by addressing him as *"Herr Doktor"*; nor was I wrong.

"How was the father's blessing, *Herr Doktor?"*

"Very fine, very fine," replied the old man in a measured, cultured voice. "Very fine, *grossartig."*

"I taught it to him," I whispered in his ear, for I suddenly felt like vaunting myself. Or maybe I just wanted to justify my presence there.

"Indeed, indeed . . . Very fine," murmured the old man politely and poured himself a glass of wine.

"He can't read Hebrew," I continued to talk scandal to him. "I had to write down the blessing for him in Latin characters. He can't even read the prayer-book. Woe to the generation. Eh?"

The old man said nothing but finished his glass.

"I suppose his grandfather was a rabbi in one of the old German communities, and yet he doesn't even know what a Hebrew letter looks like. I'm sorry for the father who brought him up like that."

"His grandfather was not a rabbi, while as for his father— he's sitting right next to you. I am his father."

It was only now that I noticed that *his* eyes squinted slightly, and that there was some slight resemblance between him and my neighbor. I flamed crimson with shame and cursed myself at heart for this sudden gush of chatter. It was impossible for me so much as to open my mouth and beg his pardon. He poured himself another glass of wine, drank it slowly to the end, and went on:

"Since you taught my son the blessing, you might as well know the whole story. His grandfather was a doctor, and I, his father, am the same. I was converted to Christianity when I was a young man, but I never was a thoroughgoing non-Jew, for I was circumcised, you know . . . I was always a sort of half-Jew and half-Gentile, a very uncomfortable position. But as for my son Richard, I never had him circumcised, for I didn't want to make his life hard for him. I wanted him to be a complete Gentile, you know . . . And now a son has been born to my son, and I was honored with the godfatherhood . . . Do you understand me properly, my dear sir? I sat there on that chair, holding the baby on my knees, and I felt that I was holding two on my knees, that I was supporting my son as well, that I was inducting him as well into the Covenant of our Father Abraham . . . Do you understand me properly, my dear sir? This was a double Covenant . . . no, no. A treble Covenant . . . I too, old man as I am, I entered the Covenant of our Father Abraham together with them. . . ."

The old man laughed in a way that was almost frightening, and wiped a tear from his eyes. That moment his son Richard came up and pressed his hand.

"*Mazel tov, Abba.*"

"*Mazel tov,*" answered the old man as he rose and left me to go with his son and bless the third to enter into the Covenant, the baby who now lay in the next room, forgetting his pain at his mother's breast.

This story, translated by I. M. Lask, appears in **Palestine Miscellany,** Tel Aviv: Zionist Organization Youth Department.

ᴥᗏ **INAUGURAL ADDRESS by Chaim Weizmann** ᔆᴥ *The momentous opening of the Knesset, the Parliament of the new state of Israel, on February 14, 1949: Chaim Weizmann, Israel's first president, speaks. . . .*

ᴥᗏ It is with a feeling of deep reverence and consecration that I rise to open the Constituent Assembly of the state of Israel—the first Knesset Israel of our time in this eternal city of Jerusalem.

This is a great moment in our history. Let us give thanks and praise to the God of Israel Who, in His mercy, granted us the privilege of witnessing the redemption of our people after centuries of affliction and suffering. Today's event issued from the great awakening of national will that aroused our people in the last few generations. The first signs came about seventy years ago.

The best among our people, men whose names were then unknown, arose to lead their generation towards fulfillment of the dream of all generations, towards the return to Zion and the restoration of Jewish nationhood. . . .

Today we stand on the threshold of a new era. We leave the dawn light of the provisional authority and enter the full sunshine of ordinary democratic rule. This Assembly was elected by a body of citizens. In the elections the will of the entire people was fully and freely expressed. From the outset we are building on solid foundations—foundations of freedom, equality, collective responsibility and national self-discipline.

It was no longer an isolated band of pioneers who elected

this Assembly, but an independent nation dwelling in its own, free country. This nation is being conceived as a gathering in of the exiles, for there is not a Jewish community throughout the world whose members have not a share in the state of Israel. . . .

In the ancient world this tiny country of ours raised the standard of spiritual revolt against the rights of tyranny and brute force. The law of Israel and the vision of her prophets sounded a new epoch of relations between man and man, a new ordering of human society. The authority of the King of Israel was limited by law and tradition. The prophets of Israel did not fear to utter rebuke and reproof to kings and princes, and with inspired words forged weapons to defend the poor and oppressed, strangers and slaves, and the orphan and the widow.

The very principle of the institution of kingship was hateful to the spiritual leaders of the people. "I will not rule over you nor shall my son rule over you. The Lord shall rule over us," declares the judge to the assembled people. The warnings of the prophet against the dangers of tyranny thunder from on high to the ears of people to our last generation.

In Israel, this authority of one man was derived from the noble conception that people are naturally free and are freely accepting the rule that law and just judgment do not need compulsion from above to live as ordered by society. The root of the principle of the constitution of that novel state was the limit set for the authority of the king and in this sense the ancient Hebrew policy was the mother of constitutional government in the modern age.

And now it has fallen to our generation to cement anew the links of that life of freedom that were snapped by tyranny's force nearly 1900 years ago. I do not know why it is precisely our generation that has been privileged to bring about what many generations before us longed for in the exiles of darkness. Unless we earned it by all the hardships, weariness, sorrow and tribulation that have been our portion during the past seventy years, when one-third of our nation was annihilated. . . .

It is our people who once gave the whole world the spiritual message fundamental to civilization. The world is watching us now to see which way we choose for ourselves in ordering our lives, and is listening to hear whether a new message will go forth from Zion, and what that message will be. The new message was not born without travail and our creative spirit. The creative force of our nation will soon meet the new, serious challenge. The Assembly is called on to frame the will for the supreme test. Let us strive in search of the basis of human life. Let us build a new bridge between science and the spirit of man.

This is a great day in our lives. Let us not be over-arrogant if we say that this is a great day in the history of the world. In this hour a message of hope and good cheer goes forth from this place in the Sacred City to all oppressed people and to all who are struggling for freedom and equality. From this place we send fraternal blessings to our brethren throughout the world and to all states, great and small, that have recognized Israel.

Excerpts from the speech as published in the **Daily News Bulletin,** New York: Jewish Telegraphic Agency, February 15, 1949.

◄§ **THE END OF DAYS** ᠗ Isaiah 2:1-4 ◄§ *In the ancient words of the Prophets, many wonderful visions were held out before the Jewish people. These hopes long ago became part of all mankind, and still live in the hearts of men. Here is the prophecy of Isaiah: Jerusalem the holy, existing under God; and the dream of universal peace, forevermore.*

◄§ And it shall come to pass in the end of days,
That the mountain of the Lord's house shall be established as
    the top of the mountains,
And shall be exalted above the hills;
And all nations shall flow unto it.
And many peoples shall go and say:
"Come ye, and let us go up to the mountain of the Lord,
To the house of the God of Jacob;
And He will teach us of His ways,
And we will walk in His paths."
For out of Zion shall go forth the Law,
And the word of the Lord from Jerusalem.
And He shall judge between the nations,
And shall decide for many peoples;
And they shall beat their swords into plowshares,
And their spears into pruning-hooks;
Nation shall not lift up sword against nation,
Neither shall they learn war any more.

VII

ON AMERICA

In the future days which we seek to make secure, we look forward to a world founded upon four essential human freedoms: freedom of speech and expression— everywhere in the world; freedom of every person to worship God in his own way—everywhere in the world; freedom from want which will secure to every nation a healthy peacetime life for its inhabitants—every- where in the world; freedom from fear, which means a world-wide reduction of armaments to such a point and in such a thorough fashion that no nation will be in a position to commit an act of physical aggres- sion against any neighbor—everywhere in the world.

Franklin D. Roosevelt

ᨀ THE ORIGIN OF THE REPUBLICAN FORM OF GOVERNMENT by Oscar S. Straus ᨀ *Oscar Straus, late nineteenth century member of the famous Straus family — lawyer, diplomat, the first American ambassador to Turkey— traces the spirit and the democratic ideals of the American Founding Fathers to their source in the Bible.*

ᨀ The Bible was to them [the Puritans] not only their guide in religion, but their text-book in politics. They studied the Old Testament and applied its teaching with a thoroughness and literal devotion that no people, excepting only the Jews, and perhaps the Scotch, had ever exemplified, for they seemed to recognize a striking similarity between their own hardships, history, and condition and those of the children of Israel under Moses and Joshua. They quoted its texts with a literal application. Their condition they characterized as "Egyptian Bondage"; James I, they styled "Pharaoh"; the ocean whose dangers and hardships their ancestors were driven to encounter they spoke of as the "Red Sea." They likened their own numbers to that of the children of Israel: "three million souls"; America in whose wilds they had come was their "Wilderness"; and in after days Washington and Adams were frequently referred to as their Moses and Joshua. Their first conception of the form of an American union was a Theocracy, the same form of government in all its essential characteristics, and expressly modelled thereafter, as the children of Israel set up over the twelve tribes under their great lawgiver Moses....The Puritans, especially the New England Puritans, evinced a greater preference for the Old Testament than perhaps they themselves were aware of....They [the ministers] mustered not only in the ranks of the Continental army, with their firelocks in hand, fighting the battles of the revolution, but on Sunday their eloquent voices were heard from the pulpit and in camp denouncing not only as false in principle, but as against the true spirit and meaning of the Scriptures, the slavish doctrines of "unlimited submission and non-resistance," which, they explained, had been invented by crown sycophants and court chaplains to flatter the ears of tyrannical rulers. They pictured in glowing words the rise and fall of the Hebrew Commonwealth, and read to their hearers again and again the warnings and admonitions of Samuel, and the references made by the prophets to the wrongs and injustice of kings, and the consequential sufferings of the people because of their rejecting God's established rule, the government of the people as it existed under Moses, Joshua, and the Judges. "And the Lord said unto Samuel, hearken unto the voice of the people in all that they say unto thee; for they have not rejected thee, but they have rejected Me, that I should not rule over them" (I Samuel 8:7). "Now therefore hearken unto their voice: howbeit yet protest solemnly unto them, and show them the manner of the king that shall reign over them" (I Sam. 8:9). These and similar passages were taken as texts for the politico-theological sermons that were heard Sunday after Sunday throughout New England.

From **The Origin of the Republican Form of Government**, by Oscar S. Straus, New York: G. P. Putnam's Sons, 1926.

◄§ **A PARABLE AGAINST PERSECUTION by Benjamin Franklin** ᙖ *Benjamin Franklin preached fervently for tolerance. To illustrate his message he created a beautiful parable in the Biblical tradition.*

◄§ And it came to pass after these things, that Abraham sat in the door of his tent, about the going down of the sun.

And behold a man, bent with age, coming from the way of the wilderness, leaning on a staff.

And Abraham arose and met him, and said unto him, "Turn in, I pray thee, and wash thy feet, and tarry all night, and thou shalt arise early in the morning, and go on thy way."

But the man said, "Nay, for I will abide under this tree."

And Abraham pressed him greatly; so he turned, and they went into the tent; and Abraham baked unleavened bread, and they did eat.

And when Abraham saw that the man blessed not God, he said unto him, "Wherefore dost thou not worship the most high God, Creator of heaven and earth?"

And the man answered and said, "I do not worship thy God, neither do I call upon His name; for I have made to myself a god, which abideth always in mine house, and provideth me with all things."

And Abraham's zeal was kindled against the man, and he arose and fell upon him, and drove him forth with blows into the wilderness.

And God called unto Abraham, saying, "Abraham, where is the stranger?"

And Abraham answered and said, "Lord, he would not worship Thee, neither would he call upon Thy name; therefore have I driven him out from before my face into the wilderness."

And God said, "Have I borne with him these hundred and ninety and eight years, and nourished him, and clothed him, notwithstanding his rebellion against Me; and couldst not thou, who art thyself a sinner, bear with him one night?"

And Abraham said, "Let not the anger of the Lord wax hot against His servant; lo, I have sinned; lo, I have sinned; forgive me, I pray Thee."

And Abraham arose, and went forth into the wilderness, and sought diligently for the man, and found him, and returned with him to the tent; and when he had entreated him kindly, he sent him away on the morrow with gifts.

And God spake again unto Abraham, saying, "For this thy sin shall thy seed be afflicted four hundred years in a strange land;

"But for thy repentance will I deliver them; and they shall come forth with power, and with gladness of heart, and with much substance."

From **The Writings of Benjamin Franklin,** edited by Albert Henry Smyth, New York: The Macmillan Company, 1906.

LETTER TO THE CONGREGATION IN NEW-PORT, RHODE ISLAND by George Washington ❧ *When the first president of the United States took office in 1790, the Jewish congregations of New York, Newport, Philadelphia, Savannah, Richmond, and Charleston sent congratulatory messages to him. Here is an excerpt from his letter to the Newport Congregation, in which he emphasizes again that religious freedom is more than a privilege; it is a right to be cherished by all citizens.*

...The Citizens of the United States of America have a right to applaud themselves for having given to mankind examples of an enlarged and liberal policy, a policy worthy of imitation.

All possess alike liberty of conscience and immunities of citizenship. It is now no more that toleration is spoken of, as if it was by the indulgence of one class of people, that another enjoyed the exercise of their inherent natural rights. For happily the Government of the United States, which gives to bigotry no sanction, to persecution no assistance, requires only that they who live under its protection should demean themselves as good citizens, in giving it on all occasions their effectual support....

May the children of the Stock of Abraham, who dwell in this land, continue to merit and enjoy the good will of the other inhabitants, while every one shall sit in safety under his own vine and fig-tree, and there shall be none to make him afraid.

This letter appears in **A Documentary History of the Jews in the United States,** edited by Morris U. Schapnes, New York: Citadel Press, 1950.

AN ORTHODOX GI FIGHTS A WAR by Gottfried Neuburger

When the author joined the United States Army during World War II, he expected a larger-than-usual share of army problems. He was an Orthodox Jew. How would he, or could he, follow the practices of his faith?

It started at once, in the improvised mess hall in the crowded induction center in Grand Central Palace. A corporal stood at the end of the chow line and looked at the large, flat metal tray I was holding.

"What's the matter? Are you sick?"

The large compartments of the tray were empty. In one of the small spaces in a corner was a helping of fruit salad, flanked by two slices of bread. The only other item was a cup of black coffee.

"No," I said, "I'm on a diet."

"You won't last long with that kind of diet."

I did not answer him, but I feared he was right....

Of course, the problem was not a new one. The saintly Chofetz Chaim had written a special book, *Camp of Israel*, on the subject of religious observance in the modern army. Still, all decisions had to be made individually, from case to case, from day to day. Fortunately there were certain rules we could go by. Under no circumstances was the Sabbath to be desecrated voluntarily or for private, non-military purposes. Sometimes it was possible to volunteer for Sunday duty in order to be off on Saturday. It was also SOP (standard operating procedure) to volunteer for KP and similar duties on Christmas and other Christian holidays. Above all we knew one thing: we had to be especially conscientious soldiers at all times. Nobody was going to be able to accuse us of using religion as a means of "gold-bricking."

And it worked....Enlisted men and officers kept the "diet," with modifications due to country or season, through North Africa and France and the Pacific, in the infantry and the combat engineers and the service units, in the army and in the navy. Strangely enough, or perhaps not so strangely, these men were not the target of anti-Semitism; they were—at least as long as the fighting lasted—treated by other soldiers and superiors alike with respect and consideration.

The whistle blew and the lights went on....I put on my drab-green army underwear, then my *arba kanfos* (Num. 15:38) and the uniform shirt and trousers. The upper floor was almost empty now. The boys knew that I shaved upstairs because I was not permitted to use a razor blade. I carried around a little arsenal of electric plugs, extension cords, and transformers to solve this problem of shaving. So far there had been no trouble. In the "tent city" at Fort Dix, on the troop train down South, and now in the infantry training center of Camp Wheeler, I had always found some electric connection where one of my plugs would fit....After a few minutes I rushed downstairs, just in time for the platoon sergeant's stentorian "Fall in!" Then came " 'Pany, 'ten-tion! Report!" On this cold December morning in Georgia it was still dark, and the stars were shining peacefully and brightly above the shivering soldiers in their heavy overcoats.

Now the men were running back into the barracks to get their messgear. On days like this I had to reverse the usual order: I ate breakfast while it was still dark and said the morning prayers afterwards. I entered the mess hall through the KP entrance. In the little storage room I picked out an orange and two raw carrots. The mess sergeant had given me the run of the space where the kitchen supplies were stacked in sacks, baskets, and bins. The company did not lose anything on the deal. A man who did not eat any meat or milk or butter, whose only cooked food was potatoes or eggs boiled in the shell whenever they happened to be on the menu, such a man—though his reasons were obscure—could have an extra can of salmon or some extra supplies any day he wanted them.

Putting on my little black skull cap, I poured water over my hands and said the blessing, "*Al netilas yodoyim.*" Taking the cap off, I walked quickly to my corner seat. That was also SOP: in each army mess hall I picked a corner seat, with my back to the wall. Though I could wear my little cap during the meals, it had to be done without any unnecessary attention—nobody was allowed to wear a uniform cap or helmet in any mess hall. Seated, I slid the cap on again and said the blessing, "Who bringeth bread forth from the earth."

There wasn't much time; first formation was at eight o'clock. For "us" it was always a race against time in the army. I got back to my bunk, saw to it that the sheets had the proper corners and that the blanket was flat and tight without any wrinkles. Then I covered my head with the *tallis*, said the blessing, put the prayer-shawl down over shoulders and back, took the cubicle coverings off the *t'fillin*—Otto Meyer always regarded these tiny velvet-lined coverings as "idols" I was praying to—and put the leather straps of the phylacteries around my head and left arm and hand (Deut. 6:8). I could say only part of the prayers; the remainder would be said during the lunch period. After all, I could not risk being caught in the middle of *Shemone esre* (prayer said three times daily, facing towards Jerusalem) when the company was marching off.

We were fully aware of the fact that we had to compromise continually. If there ever was an emergency permitting temporary religious adjustments, this war was it. The task was to hold infractions of religious observance to a minimum while keeping military efficiency at a maximum.

Saturday afternoons the camp was empty. Everybody, except the "charge of quarters," KP's, latrine orderlies, and the fellows in the guardhouse, took off. I had the whole battalion area for myself. I could not leave till sundown because I could neither sign nor carry my pass till then, and of course I could not have taken any money, even bus fare, with me. Every Sunday, however, was a sort of *hol hamoed* (semi-holiday). Within commuting distance of most camps there was usually a small town that had at least one Jewish grocery store. There we feasted on smoked fish and salami and Rokeach soups. As soldiers we had no stamps for these rationed goods, but the local Jewish Welfare Board representatives usually had some extra stamps for "institutional" purposes....

And all this time the nagging thought, "How are you going to manage when you get overseas?"

... The troop transport SS Alexander had docked an hour ago. The quay was deserted except for a handful of dock-workers and some British MP's. Now the soldiers were coming off the gangplanks, lugging their overstuffed duffelbags on their shoulders or dragging them on the ground. As if this were not enough, some of us carried an additional small wooden case....

Each of us held on doggedly to his case. This was the evening before Passover, and in the precious box we had some *matzos*, a few cans of *gefilte* fish, and even a bottle of Passover wine. (The chaplains in Camp Miles Standish and Boston Port of Embarkation had been more than thoughtful.) With the extraordinary luck of having an Orthodox chaplain on board we probably broke the U. S. Army record by having a *minyan* three times daily, with a few services in English thrown in for good measure.

There happened to be an unusually high percentage of Jews in this new outfit. Many of these boys, even though they were not very strict otherwise, wanted to have *matzos* for Passover, but there was only enough for a few. The chaplain, unfortunately, was not going to be with us any more and so I made up my mind to try to get the seasonal "bread" for all in the regiment who wanted it.

My company was billeted in Disbury. Everything and everybody was new—officers, cadre, and men....As a matter of fact, this was the first American division to be formed on foreign soil. Under the circumstances it looked almost impossible to interest the military hierarchy in the *matzos* problem.

The newly-assigned company commander proved to be open-minded on the subject. (He was a Syrian and knew a little bit about "oriental" affairs.) There was nothing he could do, but he gave me permission to see the regimental adjutant. The adjutant had other worries that morning. So he was glad when I offered to attend to everything myself. Within less than an hour I had a jeep and authorization to drive within the city limits of Manchester. Before noon I had located a large supply of *matzos* at the local Red Cross club, where it had been deposited for just such an emergency.

I loaded the big cartons into the back of the jeep. All the other companies, I found out, ate in Nissen huts like ours. During the next few hours I drove through Manchester, with a map of the city and a list of company locations in my lap, and left one box with each mess sergeant. There was no time for formal announcements or orderly procedure. I simply told each mess sergeant to place the box in a conspicuous place near the end of the chow line. Only those who had taken no bread were to be permitted to take *matzos;* otherwise there would be nothing left for those who wanted it most.

During the course of the day I had been introduced to a prominent member of the Manchester Jewish community. His wife offered to furnish me with egg, bone, herbs, and *charoses* (a special dish commemorating the period of slave-labor in Egypt), and I accepted gratefully....When I finally sat down to my Seder meal, I found that only one ingredient was missing: after just spending ten days on the Atlantic Ocean I had no salt water.

...Tonight was the birthday of the world. Tomorrow humankind would be judged for the past, each individual's fate would be inscribed for the future. "Who shall live, and who shall die, who shall find rest, and who shall be restless...."

Our convoy drove on at dawn. At the first ten-minute break I ran into the woods across a muddy field. Under my arm I clutched the *shofar* that I had brought along from England. Today the ram's horn would not be sounded the customary hundred, or even thirty, times, but the first day of Rosh Hashanah was not to pass entirely without *tekiyas shofar.* So I stood under the trees and blew the traditional tunes of *tekiyo, shevorim, teruo.* Some birds stirred in the nearby bushes—I doubt that it was applause—I wasn't that good.

A few hours later we arrived at the new seat of division headquarters....If we were to have a New Year's service for the second evening of Rosh Hashanah, immediate action was needed. I dumped my things in the newly built tent and, taking only my carbine along, went up to the castle. Near G-I (personnel, plans, and operations) I found a desk and a few olive colored trunks with marks showing that they belonged to a chaplain. Half an hour later I found him, a tall, blond, friendly captain from the Middle West. He was a Protestant.

The message center was just being organized, and field-telephone connection with the various company headquarters had not yet been established. Each company, however, had a little box at the message center which the company runners emptied at regular intervals. Through these, the companies were instructed to announce at supper that Jewish services would be held at the foot of the cascades near the castle that evening. We had twelve men at the open air services. Sergeant Berman was an excellent *hazan*. The headlights of an ambulance provided illumination. Next morning there were about twice as many participants, some of them with prayerbook and *tallis*. There was only one thing we did not have: a Sefer Torah.

Rochefort sur Ivelines, the tiny, sleepy village next to the castle grounds, was not very far from Paris. We knew that we would not move out into forward areas immediately, and so, a few days after Rosh Hashanah, the chaplain's jeep was on the way to Paris in quest of a Sefer Torah. On the trip I warned the captain that we would have to be very careful in the transport of the sacred scroll, and that if we, heaven forbid, dropped it, we would have to fast for forty days. The dignified and recently liberated gentlemen at the *Consistoire Israelite* were delighted when they heard of our request. We were referred to one of the smaller synagogues, and there the wife of the sexton led us to the Ark....

In the center of our castle there was a tremendous room, probably intended for use as a ballroom by the previous owners. I asked for permission to use it for Yom Kippur services, but I did so hesitatingly. Suppose only a handful of men came to the services! At Kol Nidre, however, the room was crowded to capacity: two hundred officers and men were there. We had enough army prayer books to go around, and everything went nicely. Next day the services started early and lasted till nightfall. The Protestant chaplain preached the sermon in the evening and in the morning; he may not have proclaimed any *hidushim* (novel rabbinical thoughts) but he touched everyone's heart.

... It took several months to finish the synagogue. The leading artisans were summoned to plan and complete the work.... The Germans could not revive the hundreds of Jews who had lived in the district; the least they could do was to assist in building this monument to their memory.

After some deliberation it was decided that the most fitting ceremony for the dedication of the new synagogue would be to hold a Bar Mitzvah ceremony for Shmuel. *Shmuel hakoton* (Samuel, the little one), as we called him, was an exception to the common rule: he had never been in a concentration camp. His parents, before being led away to camp and death, had sent their two youngest children away to pose as *Volksdeutsche*. "Never speak Yiddish as long as the Nazis are in power; never forget—even for one moment—that you are Jews." Little Shmuel had done as he was told: at the ripe old age of ten he was transported to Germany to work for a farmer who treated him like another piece of cattle.

Shmuel, now fourteen years old, was happily reunited with his sister, two years his senior, and it was high time that some belated ceremony was arranged for his Bar Mitzvah.

The crowd that gathered was as unusual as the occasion. There were a score or so of Polish-Jewish DP's, an "Aryan" Jew and his daughters, two half-Jews, a Christian widow whose Jewish husband had perished, and seven Americans, stationed nearby.

The *sudo* (festival dinner) did not have all the trimmings, and those who participated were somewhat limited in their choice of gifts. There was nothing lacking, however, in the spirit, and everybody, including Shmuel, had an extremely good time. Then someone asked for the customary speech. Shmuel rose to deliver the shortest Bar Mitzvah address I have ever heard, but I don't think any one of those present will forget it. We moved from the room into the main hall of the synagogue. When we were all seated, Shmuel went up the pulpit. He all but disappeared behind it, and only the upper half of his small dark face was visible.

"Ich bet as der tatn un di mame shoyen hereunter fun himel un sehen as ir sun vert bar mitzva haint un soln si wisn as main shvester un ich sin geblibn gute yiden di ganse yoren un mir vern imer asoi blaibn." (I pray that my mother and father may look down from heaven and see that their son is Bar Mitzvah today, and may they know that my sister and I have remained good Jews and will always remain so.)

Selections from the article in **Commentary**, March, 1949.

◄§ IN MEMORIAM: IWO JIMA by Roland B. Gittelsohn ᏇᏇ *After the grim Iwo Jima campaign of World War II, Chaplain Roland B. Gittelsohn delivered an address to dedicate the Fifth Marine Division cemetery, where lay the heroes of the bitter battle. The speech became famous throughout America.*

◄§ This is perhaps the grimmest, and surely the holiest task we have faced since D-Day. Here before us lie the bodies of comrades and friends. Men who until yesterday or last week laughed with us, joked with us, trained with us. Men who were on the same ships with us, and went over the sides with us as we prepared to hit the beaches of this island. Men who fought with us and feared with us. Somewhere in this plot of ground there may lie the man who could have discovered the cure for cancer. Under one of these Christian crosses, or beneath a Jewish Star of David, there may rest now a man who was destined to be a great prophet—to find the way, perhaps, for all to live in plenty, with poverty and hardship for none. Now they lie here silently in this sacred soil, and we gather to consecrate this earth to their memory....

No, our poor power of speech can add nothing to what these men and the other dead of our division who are not here have already done. All that we even hope to do is follow their example. To show the same selfless courage in peace that they did in war. To swear that by the grace of God and the stubborn strength and power of human will, their sons and ours shall never suffer these pains again. These men have done their job well. They have paid the ghastly price of freedom. If that free-

dom be once again lost, as it was after the last war, the unforgivable blame will be ours, not theirs. So it is we the living who
are here to be dedicated and consecrated.

We dedicate ourselves, first, to live together in peace the
way they fought and are buried in this war. Here lie men who
loved America because their ancestors generations ago helped
in her founding, and other men who loved her with equal passion because they themselves or their own fathers escaped from
oppression to her blessed shores. Here lie officers and men,
Negroes and whites, rich men and poor—together. Here are
Protestants, Catholics and Jews—together. Here no man pre-
fers another because of his faith or despises him because of his
color. Here there are no quotas of how many from each group
are admitted or allowed. Among these men there is no discrimi-
nation. No prejudices. No hatred. Theirs is the highest and
purest democracy.

Any man among us, the living, who fails to understand that
will thereby betray those who lie here dead. Whoever of us lifts
his hand in hate against a brother, or thinks himself superior
to those who happen to be in the minority, makes of this ceremony and of the bloody sacrifice it commemorates an empty,
hollow mockery. To this, then, as our solemn, sacred duty, do
we the living now dedicate ourselves: to the right of Protestants, Catholics and Jews, of white men and Negroes alike, to
enjoy the democracy for which all of them have here paid the
price....

When the last shot has been fired, there will still be those
whose eyes are turned backward, not forward, who will be satisfied with those wide extremes of poverty and wealth in which

the seeds of another war can breed. We promise you, our departed comrades: this too we will not permit. This war has been fought by the common man; its fruits of peace must be enjoyed by the common man! We promise you, by all that is sacred and holy, that your sons, the sons of miners and millers, the sons of farmers and workers, will inherit from your death the right to a living that is decent and secure....

This is part of the address as quoted in the United States **Congressional Record,** April 5, 1945.

◄§ **ACT OF FAITH by Irwin Shaw** ֍ *How do we feel about America? How do we feel about being Jews in America? A world-famous playwright, novelist, and master of the short story, born and educated in New York City, writes a gripping story about a soldier at the end of World War II, his fears and his hopes for the future, and his essential faith.*

◄§ "Present it to him in a pitiful light," Olson was saying as they picked their way through the almost frozen mud toward the orderly room tent. "Three combat-scarred veterans, who fought their way from Omaha Beach to....What was the name of the town we fought our way to?"

"Königstein," Seeger said.

"Königstein." Olson lifted his right foot heavily out of a puddle and stared admiringly at the three pounds of mud clinging to his overshoe. "The backbone of the Army. The noncommissioned officer. We deserve better of our country. Mention our decorations, in passing."

"What decorations should I mention?" Seeger asked. "The Marksman's Medal?"

"Never quite made it," Olson said. "I had a cross-eyed scorer at the butts. Mention the Bronze Star, the Silver Star, the Croix de Guerre with palms, the Unit Citation, the Congressional Medal of Honor."

"I'll mention them all," Seeger grinned. "You don't think the C.O.'ll notice that we haven't won most of them, do you?"

"Gad, sir," Olson said with dignity, "do you think that one Southern military gentleman will dare doubt the word of another Southern military gentleman in the hour of victory?"

"I come from Ohio," Seeger said.

"Welch comes from Kansas," Olson said, coolly staring down a second lieutenant who was passing. The lieutenant made a nervous little jerk with his hand, as though he expected a salute, then kept it rigid, as a slight, superior smile of scorn twisted at the corner of Olson's mouth. The lieutenant dropped his eyes and splashed on through the mud. "You've heard of Kansas," Olson said. "Magnolia-scented Kansas?"

"Of course," said Seeger. "I'm no fool."

"Do your duty by your men, Sergeant." Olson stopped to wipe the cold rain off his face and lectured him. "Highest-ranking noncom present took the initiative and saved his comrades, at great personal risk, above and beyond the call of you-know-what, in the best traditions of the American Army."

"I will throw myself in the breach," Seeger said.

"Welch and I can't ask more," said Olson.

They walked heavily through the mud on the streets between the rows of tents. The camp stretched drearily over the Reims plain, with the rain beating on the sagging tents. The division had been there over three weeks, waiting to be shipped home, and all the meager diversions of the neighborhood had been sampled and exhausted, and there was an air of watchful suspicion and impatience with the military life hanging over the camp now, and there was even reputed to be a staff sergeant in C Company who was laying odds they would not get back to America before July 4.

"I'm redeployable," Olson sang. "It's so enjoyable." It was a jingle he had composed, to no recognizable melody, in the early days after the victory in Europe, when he had added up his points and found they came to only sixty-three, but he persisted in singing it. He was a short, round boy who had been flunked out of air cadets' school and transferred to the infantry but whose spirits had not been damaged in the process. He had a high, childish voice and a pretty baby face. He was very good-natured, and had a girl waiting for him at the University of California, where he intended to finish his course at government expense when he got out of the Army, and he was just the type who is killed off early and predictably and sadly in moving pictures about the war, but he had gone through four campaigns and six major battles without a scratch.

Seeger was a large, lanky boy, with a big nose, who had been wounded at Saint-Lô but had come back to his outfit in the Siegfried Line quite unchanged. He was cheerful and dependable and he knew his business. He had broken in five or six second lieutenants, who had later been killed or wounded, and the C.O. had tried to get him commissioned in the field, but the war had ended while the paper work was being fumbled over at headquarters.

They reached the door of the orderly tent and stopped. "Be brave, Sergeant," Olson said. "Welch and I are depending on you."

"O.K.," Seeger said, and went in.

The tent had the dank, army-canvas smell that had been so much a part of Seeger's life in the past three years. The company clerk was reading an October 1945 issue of the Buffalo Courier-Express, which had just reached him, and Captain Taney, the company C.O., was seated at a sawbuck table which he used as a desk, writing a letter to his wife, his lips pursed with effort. He was a small, fussy man, with sandy hair that was falling out. While the fighting had been going on, he had been lean and tense and his small voice had been cold and full of authority. But now he had relaxed, and a little pot belly was creeping up under his belt and he kept the top button of his trousers open when he could do it without too public loss of dignity. During the war, Seeger had thought of him as a natural soldier—tireless, fanatic about detail, aggressive, severely anxious to kill Germans. But in the last few months Seeger had seen him relapsing gradually and pleasantly into the small-town hardware merchant he had been before the war, sedentary and a little shy, and, as he had once told Seeger, worried, here in the bleak champagne fields of France, about his daughter, who had just turned twelve and had a tendency to go after the boys and had been caught by her mother kissing a fifteen-year-old neighbor in the hammock after school.

"Hello, Seeger," he said, returning the salute with a mild offhand gesture. "What's on your mind?"

"Am I disturbing you, sir?"

"Oh, no. Just writing a letter to my wife. You married, Seeger?" He peered at the tall boy standing before him.

"It's very difficult." Taney sighed, pushing dissatisfiedly at the letter before him. "My wife complains I don't tell her I love her often enough. Been married fifteen years. You'd think she'd know by now." He smiled at Seeger. "I thought you were going to Paris," he said. "I signed the passes yesterday."

"That's what I came to see you about, sir."

"I suppose something's wrong with the passes." Taney spoke resignedly, like a man who has never quite got the hang of army regulations and has had requisitions, furloughs, and requests for courts-martial returned for correction in a baffling flood.

"No, sir," Seeger said. "The passes're fine. They start tomorrow. Well, it's just——" He looked around at the company clerk, who was on the sports page.

"This confidential?" Taney asked.

"If you don't mind, sir."

"Johnny," Taney said to the clerk, "go stand in the rain someplace."

"Yes, sir," the clerk said, and slowly got up and walked out.

"It's—well," said Seeger embarrassed, "it's hard to say—but it's money."

Taney shook his head sadly. "I know."

"We haven't been paid for three months, sir, and——"

"Damn it!" Taney stood up and shouted furiously. "I would like to take every bloody chair-warming old lady in the Finance Department and wring their necks."

The clerk stuck his head into the tent. "Anything wrong? You call for me, sir?"

"No!" Taney shouted. "Get out of here!"

The clerk ducked out.

Taney sat down again. "I suppose," he said, in a more normal voice, "they have their problems. Outfits being broken up, moved all over the place. But it's rugged."

"It wouldn't be so bad," Seeger said, "but we're going to Paris tomorrow. Olson, Welch, and myself. And you need money in Paris."

"Don't I know it?" Taney wagged his head. "Do you know what I paid for a bottle of champagne on the Place Pigalle in September?" He paused significantly. "I won't tell you. You wouldn't have any respect for me the rest of your life."

Seeger laughed. "Hanging is too good for the guy who thought up the rate of exchange," he said.

"I don't care if I never see another franc as long as I live."

Taney waved his letter in the air, although it had been dry for a long time.

There was silence in the tent, and Seeger swallowed a little embarrassedly. "Sir," he said, "the truth is, I've come to borrow some money for Welch, Olson, and myself. We'll pay it back out of the first pay we get, and that can't be too long from now. If you don't want to give it to us, just tell me and I'll understand and get the hell out of here. We don't like to ask, but you might just as well be dead as be in Paris broke."

Taney stopped waving his letter and put it down thoughtfully. He peered at it, wrinkling his brow, looking like an aged bookkeeper in the single gloomy light that hung in the middle of the tent.

"Just say the word, Captain," Seeger said, "and I'll blow."

"Stay where you are, son," said Taney. He dug in his shirt pocket and took out a worn sweat-stained wallet. He looked at it for a moment. "Alligator," he said, with automatic absent pride. "My wife sent it to me when we were in England. Pounds don't fit in it. However...." He opened it and took out all the contents. There was a small pile of francs on the table in front of him when he finished. He counted them. "Four hundred francs," he said. "Eight bucks."

"Excuse me," Seeger said humbly. "I shouldn't've asked."

"Delighted," Taney said vigorously. "Absolutely delighted." He started dividing the francs into two piles. "Truth is, Seeger, most of my money goes home in allotments. And the truth is, I lost eleven hundred francs in a poker game three nights ago, and I ought to be ashamed of myself. Here." He shoved one pile toward Seeger. "Two hundred francs."

Seeger looked down at the frayed, meretricious paper, which

always seemed to him like stage money anyway. "No, sir," he said. "I can't take it."

"Take it," Taney said. "That's a direct order."

Seeger slowly picked up the money, not looking at Taney. "Sometime, sir," he said, "after we get out, you have to come over to my house, and you and my father and my brother and I'll go on a real drunk."

"I regard that," Taney said gravely, "as a solemn commitment."

They smiled at each other, and Seeger started out.

"Have a drink for me," said Taney, "at the Café de la Paix. A small drink." He was sitting down to tell his wife he loved her when Seeger went out of the tent.

Olson fell into step with Seeger and they walked silently through the mud between the tents.

"Well, *mon vieux?*" Olson said finally.

"Two hundred francs," said Seeger.

Olson groaned. "Two hundred francs! That miserable, penny-loving Yankee!"

"He only had four hundred," Seeger said.

"I revise my opinion," said Olson.

They walked disconsolately and heavily back toward their tent.

Olson spoke only once before they got there. "These raincoats," he said, patting his. "Most ingenious invention of the war. Highest saturation point of any modern fabric. Collect more water per square inch, and hold it, than any material known to man. All hail the quartermaster!"

Welch was waiting at the entrance of their tent. He was standing there peering excitedly and shortsightedly out at the rain through his glasses, looking angry and tough, like a big-city hack driver, individual and incorruptible even in the ten-million colored uniform. Every time Seeger came upon Welch unexpectedly, he couldn't help smiling at the belligerent stance, the harsh stare through the steel-rimmed G.I. glasses, which had nothing at all to do with the way Welch really was. "It's a family inheritance," Welch had once explained. "My whole family stands as though we were getting ready to rap a drunk with a beer glass. Even my old lady." Welch had six brothers, all devout, according to Welch, and Seeger from time to time idly pictured them standing in a row, on Sunday mornings in church, seemingly on the verge of general violence, amid the hushed Latin and the Sabbath millinery.

"How much?" Welch asked loudly.

"Don't make us laugh," Olson said, pushing past him into the tent.

"What do you think I could get from the French for my combat jacket?" Seeger said. He went into the tent and lay down on his cot.

Welch followed them in and stood between the two of them. "Boys," he said, "on a man's errand."

"I can just see us now," Olson murmured, lying on his cot with his hands clasped behind his head, "painting Montmartre red."

"I am not worried," Welch announced.

"Get out of here." Olson turned over on his stomach.

"I know where we can put our hands on sixty-five bucks." Welch looked triumphantly first at Olson, then at Seeger.

Olson turned over slowly and sat up. "I'll kill you," he said, "if you're kidding."

"While you guys are wasting your time fooling around with the infantry," Welch said, "I used my head. I went into Reems and used my head."

"Rance," Olson said automatically. He had had two years of French in college and he felt, now that the war was over, that he had to introduce his friends to some of his culture.

"I got to talking to a captain in the Air Force," Welch said eagerly. "A little, fat old paddle-footed captain that never got higher off the ground than the second floor of Com Z headquarters, and he told me that what he would admire to do more than anything else is take home a nice shiny German Luger pistol with him to show the boys back in Pacific Grove, California."

Silence fell on the tent, and Welch and Olson looked at Seeger.

"Sixty-five bucks for a Luger these days," Olson said, "is a very good figure."

"They've been sellin' for as low as thirty-five," said Welch hesitantly. "I'll bet," he said to Seeger, "you could sell yours now and buy another one back when you got some dough, and make a clear twenty-five on the deal."

Seeger didn't say anything. He had killed the owner of the Luger, an enormous S.S. major, in Coblenz, behind some bales of paper in a warehouse, and the major had fired at Seeger three times with it, once nicking his helmet, before Seeger hit him in the face at twenty feet. Seeger had kept the Luger, a heavy, well-balanced gun, lugging it with him, hiding it at the bottom of his bedroll, oiling it three times a week, avoiding all opportunities of selling it, although he had once been offered a hundred dollars for it and several times eighty and ninety,

while the war was still on, before German weapons became a
glut on the market.

"Well," said Welch, "there's no hurry. I told the captain I'd
see him tonight around eight o'clock in front of the Lion d'Or
Hotel. You got five hours to make up your mind. Plenty of
time."

"Me," said Olson, after a pause, "I won't say anything."

Seeger looked reflectively at his feet, and the two other men
avoided looking at him.

Welch dug in his pocket. "I forgot," he said. "I picked up a
letter for you." He handed it to Seeger.

"Thanks," Seeger said. He opened it absently, thinking about
the Luger.

"Me," said Olson, "I won't say a bloody word. I'm just going
to lie here and think about that nice, fat Air Force captain."

Seeger grinned a little at him and went to the tent opening
to read the letter in the light. The letter was from his father,
and even from one glance at the handwriting, scrawly and
hurried and spotted, so different from his father's usual steady,
handsome, professorial script, he knew that something was
wrong.

"Dear Norman," it read, "sometime in the future you must
forgive me for writing this letter. But I have been holding this
in so long, and there is no one here I can talk to, and because
of your brother's condition I must pretend to be cheerful and
optimistic all the time at home, both with him and your mother,
who has never been the same since Leonard was killed. You're
the oldest now, and although I know we've never talked very
seriously about anything before, you have been through a great
deal by now, and I imagine you must have matured consider-

ably, and you've seen so many different places and people. Norman, I need help. While the war was on and you were fighting, I kept this to myself. It wouldn't have been fair to burden you with this. But now the war is over, and I no longer feel I can stand up under this alone. And you will have to face it sometime when you get home, if you haven't faced it already, and perhaps we can help each other by facing it together."

"I'm redeployable. It's so enjoyable," Olson was singing softly, on his cot. He fell silent after his burst of song.

Seeger blinked his eyes in the gray, wintry, rainy light, and went on reading his father's letter, on the stiff white stationery with the university letterhead in polite engraving at the top of each page.

"I've been feeling this coming on for a long time," the letter continued, "but it wasn't until last Sunday morning that something happened to make me feel it in its full force. I don't know how much you've guessed about the reason for Jacob's discharge from the Army. It's true he was pretty badly wounded in the leg at Metz, but I've asked around, and I know that men with worse wounds were returned to duty after hospitalization. Jacob got a medical discharge, but I don't think it was for the shrapnel wound in his thigh. He is suffering now from what I suppose you call combat fatigue, and he is subject to fits of depression and hallucinations. Your mother and I thought that as time went by and the war and the Army receded, he would grow better. Instead, he is growing worse. Last Sunday morning when I came down into the living room from upstairs he was crouched in his old uniform, next to the window, peering out."

"What the hell," Olson was saying. "If we don't get sixty-five bucks we can always go to the Louvre. I understand the Mona Lisa is back."

"I asked Jacob what he was doing," the letter went on. "He didn't turn around. 'I'm observing,' he said. 'V-1s and V-2s. Buzz bombs and rockets. They're coming in by the hundred.' I tried to reason with him and he told me to crouch and save myself from flying glass. To humor him I got down on the floor beside him and tried to tell him the war was over, that we were in Ohio, four thousand miles away from the nearest spot where bombs had fallen, that America had never been touched. He wouldn't listen. 'These're the new rocket bombs,' he said, 'for the Jews.' "

"Did you ever hear of the Pantheon?" Olson asked loudly.

"No," said Welch.

"It's free."

"I'll go," said Welch.

Seeger shook his head a little and blinked his eyes before he went back to the letter.

"After that," his father went on, "Jacob seemed to forget about the bombs from time to time, but he kept saying that the mobs were coming up the street armed with bazookas and Browning automatic rifles. He mumbled incoherently a good deal of the time and kept walking back and forth saying, 'What's the situation? Do you know what the situation is?' And once he told me he wasn't worried about himself, he was a soldier and he expected to be killed, but he was worried about Mother and myself and Leonard and you. He seemed to forget that Leonard was dead. I tried to calm him and get him back to bed before your mother came down, but he refused and wanted to set out immediately to rejoin his division. It was all terribly disjointed, and at one time he took the ribbon he got for winning the Bronze Star and threw it in the fireplace, then he got down on his hands and knees and picked it out of the ashes and made me pin it on him again, and he kept repeating, 'This is when they are coming for the Jews.' "

"The next war I'm in," said Olson, "they don't get me under the rank of colonel."

It had stopped raining by now, and Seeger folded the unfinished letter and went outside. He walked slowly down to the end of the company street, and, facing out across the empty soaked French fields, scarred and neglected by various armies, he stopped and opened the letter again.

"I don't know what Jacob went through in the Army," his father wrote, "that has done this to him. He never talks to me about the war and he refuses to go to a psychoanalyst, and from time to time he is his own bouncing, cheerful self, playing handball in the afternoons and going around with a large group of girls. But he has devoured all the concentration-camp reports, and I found him weeping when the newspapers reported that a hundred Jews were killed in Tripoli some time ago.

"The terrible thing is, Norman, that I find myself coming to believe that it is not neurotic for a Jew to behave like this today. Perhaps Jacob is the normal one, and I, going about my business, teaching economics in a quiet classroom, pretending to understand that the world is comprehensible and orderly, am really the mad one. I ask you once more to forgive me for writing you a letter like this, so different from any letter or any conversation I've ever had with you. But it is crowding me too. I do not see rockets and bombs, but I see other things.

"Wherever you go these days—restaurants, hotels, clubs,

trains—you seem to hear talk about the Jews—mean, hateful, murderous talk. Whatever page you turn to in the newspapers, you seem to find an article about Jews being killed somewhere on the face of the globe. And there are large, influential newspapers and well-known columnists who each day are growing more and more outspoken and more popular. The day that Roosevelt died I heard a drunken man yelling outside a bar, 'Finally they got the Jew out of the White House.' And some of the people who heard him merely laughed, and nobody stopped him. And on V-J Day, in celebration, hoodlums in Los Angeles savagely beat a Jewish writer. It's difficult to know what to do, whom to fight, where to look for allies.

"Three months ago, for example, I stopped my Thursday-night poker game, after playing with the same men for over ten years. John Reilly happened to say that the Jews got rich out of the war, and when I demanded an apology, he refused, and when I looked around at the faces of the men who had been my friends for so long, I could see they were not with me. And when I left the house, no one said good night to me. I know the poison was spreading from Germany before the war and during it, but I had not realized it had come so close.

"And in my economics class I find myself idiotically hedging in my lectures. I discover that I loathe to praise any liberal writer or any liberal act, and find myself somehow annoyed and frightened to see an article of criticism of existing abuses signed by a Jewish name. And I hate to see Jewish names on important committees, and hate to read of Jews fighting for the poor, the oppressed, the cheated and hungry. Somehow, even in a country where my family has lived a hundred years, the enemy has won this subtle victory over me—he has made me

disfranchise myself from honest causes by calling them foreign, Communist, using Jewish names connected with them as
ammunition against them.

"Most hateful of all, I found myself looking for Jewish
names in the casualty lists and secretly being glad when I saw
them there, to prove that there, at least, among the dead and
wounded, we belonged. Three times, thanks to you and your
brothers, I found our name there, and, may God forgive me,
at the expense of your blood and your brother's life, through
my tears, I felt that same twitch of satisfaction.

"When I read the newspapers and see another story that Jews
are still being killed in Poland, or Jews are requesting that they
be given back their homes in France or that they be allowed to
enter some country where they will not be murdered, I am
annoyed with them. I feel that they are boring the rest of the
world with their problems, that they are making demands upon
the rest of the world by being killed, that they are disturbing
everyone by being hungry and asking for the return of their
property. If we could all fall in through the crust of the earth
and vanish in one hour, with our heroes and poets and prophets
and martyrs, perhaps we would be doing the memory of the
Jewish race a service.

"This is how I feel today, son. I need some help. You've
been to the war, you've fought and killed men, you've seen the
people of other countries. Maybe you understand things that
I don't understand. Maybe you see some hope somewhere. Help
me. Your loving Father."

Seeger folded the letter slowly, not seeing what he was doing,
because the tears were burning his eyes. He walked slowly and
aimlessly across the dead, sodden grass of the empty field, away

from the camp. He tried to wipe away his tears, because, with his eyes full and dark, he kept seeing his father and brother crouched in the old-fashioned living room in Ohio, and hearing his brother, dressed in the old, discarded uniform, saying, "These're the new rocket bombs. For the Jews."

He sighed, looking out over the bleak, wasted land. Now, he thought, now I have to think about it. He felt a slight, unreasonable twinge of anger at his father for presenting him with the necessity of thinking about it. The Army was good about serious problems. While you were fighting, you were too busy and frightened and weary to think about anything, and at other times you were relaxing, putting your brain on a shelf, postponing everything to that impossible time of clarity and beauty after the war. Well, now, here was the impossible, clear, beautiful time, and here was his father, demanding that he think. There are all sorts of Jews, he thought: there are the sort whose every waking moment is ridden by the knowledge of Jewishness; who see signs against the Jew in every smile on a streetcar, every whisper; who see pogroms in every newspaper article, threats in every change of the weather, scorn in every handshake, death behind each closed door. He had not been like that. He was young, he was big and healthy and easygoing, and people of all kinds had liked him all his life, in the Army and out. In America, especially, what was going on in Europe had been remote, unreal, unrelated to him. The chanting, bearded old men burning in the Nazi furnaces, and the dark-eyed women screaming prayers in Polish and Russian and German as they were pushed naked into the gas chambers, had seemed as shadowy and almost as unrelated to him, as he trotted out onto the stadium field for a football game, as they must have been to the men named O'Dwyer and Wickersham and Poole who played in the line beside him.

These tortured people had seemed more related to him in Europe. Again and again, in the towns that had been taken back from the Germans, gaunt, gray-faced men had stopped him humbly, looking searchingly at him, and had asked, peering at his long, lined, grimy face under the anonymous helmet, "Are you a Jew?" Sometimes they asked it in English, sometimes French, sometimes Yiddish. He didn't know French or Yiddish, but he learned to recognize that question. He had never understood exactly why they asked the question, since they never demanded anything of him, rarely even could speak to him. Then, one day in Strasbourg, a little bent old man and a small shapeless woman had stopped him and asked, in English, if he was Jewish. "Yes," he'd said, smiling at them. The two old people had smiled widely, like children. "Look," the old man had said to his wife. "A young American soldier. A Jew. And so large and strong." He had touched Seeger's arm reverently with the tips of his fingers, then had touched the Garand Seeger was carrying. "And such a beautiful rifle."

And there, for a moment, although he was not particularly sensitive, Seeger had got an inkling of why he had been stopped and questioned by so many before. Here, to these bent, exhausted old people, ravaged of their families, familiar with flight and death for so many years, was a symbol of continuing life. A large young man in the uniform of the liberator, blood, as they thought, of their blood, but not in hiding, not quivering in fear and helplessness, but striding secure and victorious down the street, armed and capable of inflicting terrible destruction on his enemies.

Seeger had kissed the old lady on the cheek and she had wept, and the old man had scolded her for it while shaking Seeger's hand fervently and thankfully before saying good-bye.

And, thinking back on it, it was silly to pretend that, even before his father's letter, he had been like any other American soldier going through the war. When he had stood over the huge dead S.S. major with the face blown in by his bullets in the warehouse in Coblenz, and taken the pistol from the dead hand, he had tasted a strange little extra flavor of triumph. How many Jews, he'd thought, has this man killed, how fitting it is that I've killed him. Neither Olson nor Welch, who were like his brothers, would have felt that in picking up the Luger, its barrel still hot from the last shots its owner had fired before dying. And he had resolved that he was going to make sure to take this gun back with him to America, and plug it and keep it on his desk at home, as a kind of vague, half-understood sign to himself that justice had once been done and he had been its instrument.

Maybe, he thought, maybe I'd better take it back with me, but not as a memento. Not plugged, but loaded. America by now was a strange country for him. He had been away a long time and he wasn't sure what was waiting for him when he got home. If the mobs were coming down the street toward his house, he was not going to die singing and praying.

When he had been taking basic training, he'd heard a scrawny, clerkish soldier from Boston talking at the other end of the PX bar, over the watered beer. "The boys at the office," the scratchy voice was saying, "gave me a party before I left. And they told me one thing. 'Charlie,' they said, 'hold onto your bayonet. We're going to be able to use it when you get back. On the Yids.' "

He hadn't said anything then, because he'd felt it was neither possible nor desirable to fight against every random overheard voice raised against the Jews from one end of the world to the other. But again and again, at odd moments, lying on a barracks cot, or stretched out trying to sleep on the floor of a ruined French farmhouse, he had heard that voice, harsh, satisfied, heavy with hate and ignorance, saying above the beery grumble of apprentice soldiers at the bar, "Hold on to your bayonet."

And the other stories. Jews collected stories of hatred and injustice and inklings of doom like a special, lunatic kind of miser. The story of the navy officer, commander of a small vessel off the Aleutians, who in the officers' wardroom had complained that he hated the Jews because it was the Jews who had demanded that the Germans be beaten first, and the forces in the Pacific had been starved in consequence. And when one of his junior officers, who had just come aboard, had objected and told the commander that he was a Jew, the commander had risen from the table and said, "Mister, the Constitution of the United States says I have to serve in the same Navy with Jews, but it doesn't say I have to eat at the same table with them." In the fogs and the cold, swelling Arctic seas off the Aleutians, in a small boat, subject to sudden, mortal attack at any moment....And the million other stories. Jews, even the most normal and best adjusted, became living treasuries of them, scraps of malice and bloodthirstiness, clever and confusing and cunningly twisted so that every act by every Jew became suspect and blameworthy and hateful. Seeger had heard the stories and had made an almost conscious effort to forget them. Now, holding his father's letter in his hand, he remembered them all.

He stared unseeingly out in front of him. Maybe, he thought.

maybe it would've been better to have been killed in the war, like Leonard. Simpler. Leonard would never have to face a crowd coming for his mother and father. Leonard would not have to listen and collect these hideous, fascinating little stories that made of every Jew a stranger in any town, on any field, on the face of the earth. He had come so close to being killed so many times; it would have been so easy, so neat and final. Seeger shook his head. It was ridiculous to feel like that, and he was ashamed of himself for the weak moment. At the age of twenty-one, death was not an answer.

"Seeger!" It was Olson's voice. He and Welch had sloshed silently up behind Seeger, standing in the open field. "Seeger," *mon vieux*, what're you doing—grazing?"

Seeger turned slowly to them. "I wanted to read my letter," he said.

Olson looked closely at him. They had been together so long, through so many things, that flickers and hints of expression on each other's faces were recognized and acted upon. "Anything wrong?" Olson asked.

"No," said Seeger. "Nothing much."

"Norman," Welch said, his voice young and solemn. "Norman, we've been talking, Olson and me. We decided—you're pretty attached to that Luger, and maybe, if you—well——"

"What he's trying to say," said Olson, "is we withdraw the request. If you want to sell it, O.K. If you don't, don't do it for our sake. Honest."

Seeger looked at them standing there, disreputable and tough and familiar. "I haven't made up my mind yet," he said.

"Anything you decide," Welch said oratorically, "is perfectly all right with us. Perfectly."

The three of them walked aimlessly and silently across the field, away from camp. As they walked, their shoes making a wet sliding sound in the damp, dead grass, Seeger thought of the time Olson had covered him in a little town outside Cherbourg, when Seeger had been caught, going down the side of a street, by four Germans with a machine gun in the second story of a house on the corner and Olson had to stand out in the middle of the street with no cover at all for more than a minute, firing continuously, so that Seeger could get away alive. And he thought of the time outside Saint-Lô when he had been wounded and had lain in a minefield for three hours and Welch and Captain Taney had come looking for him in the darkness and had found him and picked him up and run for it, all of them expecting to get blown up any second. And he thought of all the drinks they'd had together, and the long marches and the cold winter together, and all the girls they'd gone out with together, and he thought of his father and brother crouching behind the window in Ohio waiting for the rockets and the crowds armed with Browning automatic rifles.

"Say." He stopped and stood facing them. "Say, what do you guys think of the Jews?"

Welch and Olson looked at each other, and Olson glanced down at the letter in Seeger's hand.

"Jews?" Olson said finally. "What're they? Welch, you ever hear of the Jews?"

Welch looked thoughtfully at the gray sky. "No," he said. "But remember, I'm an uneducated fellow."

"Sorry, but," Olson said, turning to Seeger, "we can't help you. Ask us another question. Maybe we'll do better."

Seeger peered at the faces of his friends. He would have to

rely upon them, later on, out of uniform, on their native streets, more than he had ever relied on them on the bullet-swept street and in the dark minefield in France. Welch and Olson stared back at him, troubled, their faces candid and tough and dependable.

"What time," Seeger asked, "did you tell that captain you'd meet him?"

"Eight o'clock," Welch said. "But we don't have to go. If you have any feeling about that gun——"

"We'll meet him," Seeger said. "We can use that sixty-five bucks."

"Listen," Olson said, "I know how much you like that gun, and I'll feel like a heel if you sell it."

"Forget it," Seeger said, starting to walk again. "What could I use it for in America?"

This story was first published in the **New Yorker** magazine.

◄§ VISION FOR AMERICAN JEWS by Milton Steinberg ৪►
*A stirring dream of American Jewry, from one of the important
books on Jewish life in our day.*

◄§ I see in Palestine a Jewish Commonwealth where the homeless Jews of the world have found rest, where the Jewish spirit
has been reborn, whence flow to the Dispersion inspiration and
the stuffs on which it feeds.

I see the Jewries of the world, each at ease and firmly rooted
in the land of its residence, each unswervingly devoted to the
polity and culture of that land and at the same time the bearer
and transmitter of a living Hebraism, significant to itself, its
environment and the world.

Most specifically, I see an American Jewry, emancipated
along with all other Americans from the restraints of prejudice,
secure against violence, free to fulfill itself without hindrance.

An American Jewry alight with a religious faith hallowed by
antiquity and responsive to the mystery of all things, yet
sanctioned by the best in modern thought and clean with
reasonableness.

An American Jewry standing four square by Judaism's great
moral ideals, sharpening them into the keenest contemporane-
ousness, applying them boldly, imaginatively—so that the name
Jew is a synonym for the practice and advocacy of justice, compassion, freedom and peace.

An American Jewry literate in both its heritages, the American and Hebraic, creative in both, cross-blending and fertiliz-
ing the two until all devotion to one shall connote blessing
for the other as well.

An American Jewry that in its observances is both reverential of the tradition and awake to current needs, so that the precious freightage of the past is enriched by new gifts in each generation.

An American Jewry whose household is set in order.

An American Jewry which, having labored that Zion be rebuilt, now draws waters in joy from the fountainhead of the Jewish spirit.

I see in sum a Jewry which in its inner life has made of Judaism what it is intended to be, what it is now in some measure, and what it can become in infinitely greater degree—that is to say, a source of blessing.

And I see all this set in a new, brave and free world which Jews, together with all men of good will, have helped to set free, laboring as individuals but also as Jews, as members of a fellowship consecrated from the womb to the ideal of a new, brave and free world.

Should that day arrive, should a better ordering of human affairs be won, and from its elevation a backward glance be cast over mankind's long, weary pilgrimage, what answer then will be appropriate to our question....

Shall not Jewish dreams and ideals, hands and hearts, blood and anguish have contributed to this end so long desired and prayed for? Will it then be a little thing—will it not rather be accounted a very great thing—to have played a part, not the largest perhaps but not the meanest either, in the building of the Kingdom of God on earth?

From **A Partisan Guide to the Jewish Problem,** by Milton Steinberg, Indianapolis: The Bobbs-Merrill Company, 1945.

VIII

BAR MITZVAH STORIES

For this commandment which I command thee this day, it is not too hard for thee, neither is it far off.

It is not in heaven, that thou shouldest say: "Who shall go up for us to heaven, and bring it unto us to hear it, that we may do it?"

Neither is it beyond the sea, that thou shouldest say: "Who shall go over the sea for us, and bring it unto us, and make us to hear it, that we may do it?"

But the word is very nigh unto thee, in thy mouth, and in thy heart, that thou mayest do it.

Deuteronomy

◄§ BAR MITZVAH IN SPAIN by A. A. Kabak §► *There was a time when participation in a Bar Mitzvah ceremony was a crime punishable by death. A prominent Hebrew writer tells a story of the 15th century, in the days of the Spanish Inquisition.*

◄§ Pierce was only about five years old at the time, but the memory of that dreadful day remains with him always. He remembers his father and mother, pale and trembling with fear, taking him into a dark cave near their home. They begged him not to cry or make a sound, lest evil men, hearing his voice, should come and kill him. They promised him that in a little while, a very little while, their servant, Ferdinand, would come and fetch him from the cave. He remained alone in the darkness, his eyes following his father and mother whom he was seeing for the last time. They called goodbye from the mouth of the cave, standing there hunched over, looking at him.

For many a day, his father's voice rang in his ears: "My son, you will be a Jew—a Jew all your life!"

His mother cried, and pleaded in a broken voice: "My son, will you remember your mother? Tell me, will you remember your mother?"

The dear caressing voices vanished; the dear pale faces disappeared. The opening of the cave was closed. He was alone in the darkness. He lost consciousness.

When he opened his eyes, he found himself in his own room, in Ferdinand's arms. The boy's heart was full of fear. He still saw the blackness of the cave around him.

As the days passed, he enjoyed sitting in the old servant's

lap. The world seemed safe from underneath Ferdinand's white beard. But at night—at night darkness covered the land, the world was full of raving evil spirits, ferocious beasts who wanted to kill him. Then the lad would find a warm refuge in Ferdinand's bed. He would listen to the old man's stories of magicians and witches, heroes and villains, heaven and hell. Terrifying stories, but it was nice to hear them with the good old man lying beside him and protecting him with his presence.

Then, it all suddenly ceased, like a dream. Little Pierce didn't know how it happened. One morning he found himself in the monastery. Many boys were there, and young monks and old monks, all in long, black cloaks.

When the boys were by themselves, they would laugh and play. But little Pierce was sad and frightened. He felt the same fear as in the dark cave. At night he would lie in his bed, hide his face in the pillow, and longingly remember Ferdinand. He would hear in his imagination Ferdinand's soothing voice, telling him enchanting stories.

The boy moved among his comrades like a young monk— pale, sad, silent. Every Sunday afternoon the students would assemble in the auditorium, or in the garden among the trees. Antonius, the friar, would tell them about the saints—the many trials they had suffered in their lifetime, the miracles God had wrought for them. Pierce thirstily absorbed all that Antonius said. He thought of all the sorrows that had befallen him, and prayed that God would also work miracles for him.

One day in the garden Pierce saw Antonius speaking to an old monk who had just arrived at the monastery. Pierce passed near them, and heard the old man's voice. He stopped and listened intently. Where had he heard that voice before, he wondered. He knew he had heard it—but where? When?

He looked at the man's face. A strange face, yet it seemed to him he had seen it before. He stood quite still, peering at the old monk's face. He tried to remember—where had he seen him?

The two men noticed the boy, and stopped their conversation.

"Why are you standing here?" called the friar. "Go to your room and memorize the passage I assigned you."

Pierce went to his room, but he could not study a single line. He could not forget the old monk's face and voice. Who was he? He was surer than ever that he had once heard that voice, seen that face. But when? Where?

In the middle of the night he fell asleep. Suddenly he awoke, frightened. The old man stood beside his bed, holding a candle. For a moment Pierce thought he was dreaming, but the old man spoke.

"Get up! The head monk is calling for you."

"Why is he calling? Have I disobeyed in some way?"

"Go to his room. You will find out there."

Who knows what new trouble I'll find there, thought the lad. With trembling hands he dressed, praying for a miracle. The old man opened the door, the boy followed him.

It was very black in the corridor. Pierce began to wonder. He knew that usually there was a light in the hall at night. The darkness heightened the boy's fear. Why no light in the corridor tonight? Where was the old man taking him? What would they do to him?

For a long time he followed the old man through the blackness of many corridors. The old man made no sound, and the poor lad was afraid to ask anything. He followed, weeping silently, swallowing his tears.

At last they came to a room. A small candlestick stood on the table. The old man raised the candlestick to his face, and a glad welcome filled the chamber.

"Who are you?" cried the boy in a quavering voice.

"Look at me, son! Don't you recognize me?"

"I'm sure I've seen you before, but I don't recognize you. Who are you?"

The old man caught the boy up in his arms, embraced him lovingly. "I'm Ferdinand—Ferdinand—your faithful servant!"

"Ferdinand!" cried the boy. And tears rolled from his eyes.

That night his old friend revealed to the boy the secret of his past. His parents were Jewish, Ferdinand told him. They had sanctified God's name before the Tribunal of the Inquisition, choosing death rather than give up their faith. Ferdinand told him of his parents' goodbye in the blackness of the cave. Pierce had forgotten the whole terrible incident that had happened to him as a child of five. Now those bitter memories returned, to stand out vividly in his mind.

Ferdinand also told of his own experiences—of trials and dangers he had undergone since they had parted. Now he had come back to Pierce, and he would never leave him. The danger was great—but there was no other choice. Pierce's parents had appeared to Ferdinand in a dream, had commanded him to go to the monastery and bring their son back to the faith of Israel.

"If the spies of the Inquisition discover our secret," said Ferdinand, "we shall be burned at the stake. But there is no other way, Pierce! We have no choice but to walk the way of the Lord God, the God of your fathers. It is a road full of sorrow and danger. But it is also the way to redemption and sal-vation. Your saintly parents trod that path and died, and you too, my son, must follow it. You must be prepared for any-thing. The time has not yet come, Pierce, for me to reveal everything to you, but this I can tell you: thousands upon thousands of your brethren are secretly following the road of the Lord, their God. Braving death, they pray for redemption and salvation. They are ready at any time to sanctify the name of God, just as your parents did."

Ferdinand's words were new and wonderful to Pierce. He looked up at the old man with big bewildered eyes. With beating heart he listened to the whispering voice.

From that fateful day on, the boy would get up each night and walk through the dark corridors to Ferdinand's cell. There they would sit together over a Hebrew book, and secretly learn Torah. Thus Ferdinand prepared the boy for the day when he would become Bar Mitzvah. On that day Pierce would enter the sacred covenant of his people. He would become a member of the community of Israel, which, like him, worshiped the God of their fathers in secret. Pierce awaited that day expectantly.

The night before the big day, Ferdinand reviewed all the prayers and blessings of the Bar Mitzvah ceremony. Ferdinand asked Pierce if he was ready to accept the grave responsibility of loyalty to his people and his God.

Pierce, in a firm voice, "Yes!"

In the morning, the monastery bells called everyone to prayer. How frightening these bells sounded to Pierce that morning! He accompanied the other boys to the monastery chapel. As they lustily sang the morning prayers, his lips whis-pered a Hebrew prayer to the God of his fathers—a prayer he had learned by heart at night from Ferdinand's lips.

After breakfast they told him Don Francisco Henriques had come to take him to his house for the day. Pierce was bewildered, frightened. He knew Don Henriques was one of the wealthy men of Lisbon. Pierce had often heard the monks bless him for being one of the faithful followers of the Church. Why had this man suddenly come to take him home? Today of all days! The great, the holy day, for which he had been waiting so long! What would Ferdinand say, and all the people waiting for him in some unknown place?

He was still turning it over in his mind and weeping in his heart when he heard his name called. Anxiously Pierce rose, and approached the monk who called him. Near the monk stood a tall, handsome nobleman. Pierce greeted him, bowing.

"Who are you, boy?" asked the man.

"Diego Pierce—the son of Don Salvador and Dona Angelica Pierce, peace to their souls!"

"Fine, Diego! And I am Don Francisco Henriques. I was a good friend of your parents—may they rest in peace! I have come to take you to my home for a visit."

His face and voice warmed the boy's heart. But how could he go with him, on this, the greatest and holiest day of his life?

"I'll go ask the abbot for permission," said Pierce. A sudden hope flared in his heart that Antonius would not allow him to go.

"I already have Father Antonius' permission," said Don Henriques.

The words fell on the boy's ear like stones.

They left the monastery.

During the whole journey they did not exchange a word.

Don Henriques rode as a rich man should, on a beautiful horse. After him rode the boy, in monk's dress, on a little mule.

In a wealthy section of the town, they stopped at a beautiful palace. Frightened and trembling, Pierce followed the big man. The door opened, and they entered a big room. The boy was afraid to raise his eyes. He stood still, head hanging, his body full of misery. Then he felt a gentle hand on his head, and a familiar voice called his name.

The boy looked up and saw Ferdinand standing beside him. Pierce's face glowed with joy. With Ferdinand there, he had nothing to fear! Then he saw people seated around the room, all silent. Why were they quiet? What were they waiting for?

A servant entered the room, whispered something in Don Henriques' ear. Don Henriques gave a signal and everyone rose from his seat. The host led the way, holding Pierce's hand. The rest followed.

They passed through many chambers until they reached a small room with closets lining the walls. Don Henriques opened a closet and entered it with the boy. The closet wall opened, and they were in a big pit.

"Be careful, my son," said Don Henriques. "We have to go down some steps here."

In the darkness they descended many steps. The boy's heart trembled. Where is he leading me? The memory of the dark cave where his parents had taken him swept over him. He wanted to burst out into tears, but suddenly he saw a light. They were in a large cellar, where candles burned in candlesticks and men stood wrapped in white *talleitim*. The boy was filled with joy and fear.

They gave him a prayer shawl, in which he wrapped himself.

He felt a great gladness. This, indeed, was the big day about which Ferdinand had told him. His day!

A deep, strong voice filled the room.

"Praise the Lord and let us exalt His name!"

Pierce recognized the voice and grew faint. Antonius—the head of the monastery! He had fallen into a trap! Ferdinand and Don Henriques had plotted against him! They would burn him at the stake! But after a moment, he grew calm. He saw Antonius, wrapped in a *tallit*, standing on the platform, and in his arms a Torah. Antonius put the Torah on the table, opened it, began to read from it.

"And it shall come to pass, if you listen to the voice of the Lord, thy God, and keep and obey all His commandments . . ."

He chanted the words with great feeling and in beautiful melody. The sound entered deep into the boy's soul, like a bright holy light.

Pierce closed his eyes. It seemed to him he was dreaming a sweet dream. He could not believe that Antonius and Don Henriques were Jews too.

He looked at the congregation sitting here in the cellar, listening, with a holy glow on their faces, to the words of the Torah. They were all his people—Jews. Brave Jews, daring death and disaster to be true to their faith.

He remembered what Ferdinand had said about the path to the God of Israel—a path of sorrow and danger, but also a path to redemption and salvation. Here they were, treading this path, and he, Pierce, was one of them.

There was sudden silence in the cellar. Pierce sat erect. Everyone was looking at him.

Antonius called, "Rise, Solomon, son of Meshulam Molkho!"

His heart said to him—"that's your name, Pierce; that and
no other. They are calling you to the Torah. Go up!" Head
high he went up—in the path of the God of Israel.

Later Antonius spoke to him, his voice sounding like a song,
like a prayer. "Today you have joined the covenant of God and
our people. You are taking upon yourself the holy duty of
keeping the words of this Torah and walking in the path of
your parents and forefathers. You have chosen it willingly. May
you follow it all the days of your life!"

The picture of his childhood came to him vividly. He saw
his father and mother standing in the mouth of the cave, he
heard their voices.

"My son—you will remain a Jew—a Jew all your life. What
did your father tell you? Who are you?"

"A Jew, Mother."

"Tell me again, my dear one."

"A Jew, Mother."

"Again, my beloved!"

"A Jew, Mother!"

The boy placed his hand on the Torah. "I swear it!" he cried
in a strong, firm voice. "Amen, amen!"

From **Solomon Molkho,** Volume I, by A.A. Kabak, London: Haolam, 1927;
translated by Sora I. Eisenberg.

◦§ **BAR MITZVAH JOY** by David Cohen ◦ *Another wonderful story of the Baal Shem Tov, told by a contemporary writer from Israel.*

◦§ It was the custom of the Baal Shem Tov to journey by wagon to remote settlements, and bring the hearts of the simple folk of Israel closer to God. One time he came upon a distant settlement cut off from any city or town. The people of the place were very simple Jews, villagers, workers of the fields and the forest. They toiled very hard, and had time only for a snatched prayer at *Shacharit*, *Mincha* and *Maarev*. And even then they did not know the meaning of the words. They would bemoan their loneliness, and saw themselves as outcasts, abandoned by the rest of Israel.

Among the people of the settlement there was one, a tax-collector, rich and respected, who was recognized as their leader and head. This tax-collector had an only son, who did not go about with the rest of the Jewish boys, for they knew no Torah, and besides, they were laborers, just like their fathers. And when this boy became thirteen years old, his father, the tax-collector, called a big feast, and invited all the Jews of the village. They dressed themselves in their Sabbath best, and came to the Bar Mitzvah celebration.

At that time the Baal Shem Tov was traveling in the neighborhood. The tax-collector came before him, and begged him to honor the occasion with his presence. The Baal Shem Tov accepted. He came and sat at the head of the table, and studied the weather-beaten faces of the villagers, their black, gnarled hands. They sat at the table, covered with all good things, like apprehensive children, afraid of their elders. The heart of the Baal Shem Tov went out in pity to these simple folk. He began to delight them with beautiful *Nigunim*, the melodies of shepherds in the Carpathian hills, and with pleasing tales. The villagers drank in every note of the *Nigun*, and every word of the story. Their happy faces shone, and they fingered their grizzled beards. Tears of joy sparkled in their eyes. The tax-collector saw all this, and was filled with anger and amazement at the Baal Shem Tov for not talking to him or to his son, who after all had the true spirit of the Torah. Instead, he paid attention only to the coarse villagers, who were not even fit to be called human beings. The tax-collector, anxious to rebuke the Baal Shem Tov, stood up and announced: "All that we have eaten and drunk up until now is only a beginning, merely the introduction. The real feast will begin upon the arrival of the Rabbi, and the honored guests from the distant town. Only before them will the Bar Mitzvah deliver his *droshe*, the interpretation of the Torah. Only they are fit to hear the words of the Torah."

The Baal Shem Tov pretended not to hear. He turned to the Bar Mitzvah boy, and regaled him with Torah and ethics. He awakened in the boy's heart a love for the Creator. While his words were sinking into the boy's thoughts, the Baal Shem Tov glued his eyes on the open window, towards the broad stretches of field and forest. He concentrated on a far, faraway point. The villagers watched the face of the Baal Shem Tov change. Slowly his face changed color, and, then, suddenly, he burst

into a hearty laugh. He laughed once, twice, and the laugh
sounded like an outburst from the innermost depths. His face
laughed, his eyes laughed, his beard laughed. The simple village folk, drawn in by this laughter, began too to laugh. And
it seemed as if everything was laughing: the fields, the forest,
the lake, even the heavens above, and the burning sun—all the
world joined in a hearty ringing laugh. And the Baal Shem Tov
was making all sorts of strange movements and grimaces. He
neighed like a horse, and mooed like a cow, crowed like a
rooster and bleated like a sheep. And all, all were convulsed
in laughter.

At that moment a carriage drew near, and in it was the Rabbi
of the town, together with his retinue. When they entered the
house, they heard the laughter, and the sounds of the beasts of
house and field. They were frightened and inquired: "What is
the meaning of all this?" Then the Baal Shem Tov told them
what he had seen.

"In a distant village, lying at the foot of the Carpathian
Mountains, there dwells a widow with an only son, and today
is the day of his Bar Mitzvah. The boy never studied Torah,
for the village is very far from any settlement. But he donned
the *Tefillin*, the phylacteries which his father left him as an
inheritance. He wound them around his arm, and placed them
on his forehead, just as his father had taught him to do. His
mother had told him that it was a custom among Jews for the
Bar Mitzvah boy to be called up before the congregation to
read from the Torah, and that a *Minyan*, a quorum of Jews,
must listen to the Blessings, and answer: Amen. The boy listened to his mother's words carefully. He went into the barn,

and gathered all the barnyard animals and fowl. With his great love he brought them all together, and they constituted his *Minyan*. He smoothed the horse's mane, stroked the back of the cow, patted the goat and the dog. The boy stood in their midst, and the animals, the congregation, heard from his own lips the good news that today he was being received into the Law. The animals answered Amen, each in their own way, with a neighing, a bleating, a braying and a barking. The angels heard this, and they too joined in with their Amen. Their joy and laughter rolled from heaven to heaven, and ascended to the Holy Seat itself."

The Baal Shem Tov concluded. He turned to the Rabbi, to all those present, and to the Bar Mitzvah boy, and said: "Because of the orphan boy from the Carpathian Mountains, the very gates of Heaven are open. Come, now let us hear the Bar Mitzvah's *droshe!*"

From **Asher Shamati Vesiparti,** by David Cohen, Tel Aviv: Hakibutz Hameti-had, 1946; this translation by Maier Deshell appeared in **Haboneh** Magazine, March 1950.

◈ A CAUCASIAN BAR MITZVAH by Yehuda Burla ❧
Between Europe and Asia, in the wild and isolated mountains of Caucasia, there is a community of Jews. It has been described by a renowned Jerusalem-born Sephardic Hebrew writer, in his book, Adventures of Akavyah. *For hundreds of years the Jews of this country lived a hard and primitive life, separated from civilization as we know it, providing for themselves as herdsmen and mountaineers. And yet as in the world over, when a young man approaches the age of Bar Mitzvah. . . .*

◈ It was winter when Akavyah's father brought him to the teacher once more. Akavyah's eyes, expert in finding the narrow winding paths along the precipices and the lofty Caucasian peaks, could not find their way through the small Hebrew type. With great pain and great difficulty, the teacher taught him to read the prayers and the blessings. But as soon as the winter passed, Akavyah and his father were off again to the mountains....

When the day of Akavyah's Bar Mitzvah drew near, his father begged the teacher to prepare a speech for his son. He would pay the señor *haham* whatever was necessary.

The teacher replied gently: "A speech is unnecessary. Akavyah will put on his *tefillin* without a speech."

The father insisted. "When I was Bar Mitzvah," he said, "I, too, had a hard head. But my *haham* drilled the speech into me. This I know: it was worth it. From it I learned what Judaism means. I remember my speech; it entered me as new blood. It was a transfusion of faith. It gave me love for God and Torah. And this is why I want a speech for my son."

"How did you deliver your speech? And in what language, Ladino or Hebrew?"

"Ladino, of course. Each day, for many weeks and months, my teacher asked questions, and taught me to answer them. That is how I learned: question, answer; question, answer. Can't you teach Akavyah the same way?"

And so the teacher consented. If the father's teacher could do it, the son's teacher could do it too.

For three months the teacher drilled Akavyah. It was like chiseling rock. But little by little, he cut grooves into Akavyah's mind. It was hard work but the goal was finally achieved.

On the day of the party, late Sunday morning, Señor Hasdai's house was crowded with guests: prominent *hahamim*, men of affairs, relatives, neighbors, acquaintances. Quite truthfully, many of them came to be entertained by the novelty of hearing Akavyah make a speech.

Akavyah had spent the whole morning at his teacher's house practicing his speech. Dressed in a new, high turban, his silk robe held together by a wide sash, he returned home and was surprised by the crowd. His father and mother had promised that just a few relatives would be present; now he could not begin to count the vast crowd.

The *haham* hung on to Akavyah's arm and pulled him along like a lamb being led to the slaughter. Akavyah's face was pale. His eyes searched for his father. Teacher and pupil finally reached the place of honor, the bench near the open window where Akavyah was to deliver his "speech."

Akavyah turned to his father and accused him:

"So this is what my father has done! This is the promise he made! This is how he fooled me!" Then Akavyah leaped through the window, tucked the bottom of his robe into his sash, and ran away.

Astonished and embarrassed, the guests were about to leave when Señor Hasdai's voice was heard.

"Don't be disturbed, dear friends. You will yet hear the speech and partake of the party. The bird has flown by way of the window. But he will come back by way of the door. Believe me, my son is a good boy. He flares up like a flame in a stack of straw; it burns fast and is consumed fast. The *haham* and I will bring him back. Meanwhile let the singers entertain you."

He left the house together with the *haham*. They got into the carriage and off they rode to the mountains. At the foot of the mountains, under the hot rays of the sun, they found Akavyah.

The father began in soothing and endearing tones: "Akavyah, dear heart, why have you shamed us so? To run off before your speech! If you wanted to run away, why did you not wait until after the speech?"

Akavyah replied angrily: "Why was I fooled? Why wasn't the promise kept that I would speak only before relatives? Why was the whole world invited to the house? Is it right to lie? Can it be that the *haham* and father would tell an untruth? Is Akavyah a rabbi that he should preach to a congregation?"

The father admitted his wrong and asked for forgiveness. He had no choice but to invite the señores and *hahamim*. It would have been unforgivable not to invite them. The others came without invitations. Does Akavyah want him to drive them out? And moreover, what difference is there really if he speaks to three or to thirty? Will anyone ask that he say more than he is prepared to say?

But Akavyah remained obstinate. He had been deceived. Let the *haham* speak for him.

Then the father gave his last and most convincing argument: Let Akavyah do it for the sake of mother...Akavyah returned for the sake of mother.

It was midafternoon when they arrived at the house. The singers were still entertaining the guests. Akavyah wrapped himself in a big *tallit* and put on his *tefillin*.

When the time came for his speech the *haham* sat down on a bench facing Akavyah, with his back to the guests.

The *haham* began in Spanish. At the sound of his voice Akavyah rocked lightly on his feet, as if he were sparring with another fighter. His brow was wrinkled and his eyes were fixed on the *haham*.

"Tell me, dear heart, these *tefillin* that you wear today, what are they?"

Mechanically, automatically, the words came out of Akavyah's mouth:

"The *tefillin* are the flag of our people. We owe them allegiance as to a flag."

"A flag, you say? But I don't see a pole, or a rope, or a cloth. How are *tefillin* like a flag?"

"Every flag bears the symbol of its people. There are red flags; they symbolize blood, war. There are flags bearing the symbol of a lion; they stand for courage, and so on. The *tefillin*, our flag, symbolize the quality of Israel."

"What symbol are you talking about? And where is it shown?"

"Here: *Shaddai.*" Akavyah pointed to the letter on the headpiece.

"And what is the meaning of *Shaddai?*"

"*Shalom degel Yisrael*—Peace is the flag of Israel."

"Well said, Akavyah. Now tell us whom the flag honors."

"The ruler of the people."

"And who is our ruler?"

"The King of Kings, the Almighty, blessed be His name."

"And what does it teach us?"

"That Israel is a holy people."

"And do you know what is in these boxes?"

"They contain the Torah reading. 'And thou shalt love Thy God.'..."

In this manner the *haham* evoked Akavyah's "speech" on the themes of love, faith, truth, peace, and justice. Father and mother glowed with joy; their eyes shed tears of happiness. All the guests applauded.

It was then that everyone realized that Akavyah was not as hard as rock but that he was a lad of charm and sweetness, of character, and that he would grow to fine manhood.

From **Alilot Akavyah (Adventures of Akavyah)**, by Yehudah Burla, Tel Aviv: Dvir, 1947; translated by A. E.

A BAR MITZVAH SPEECH by Sholom Aleichem
One of the greatest Yiddish writers of recent years, whose real name is Solomon Rabinowitz (1859-1916), looks back upon his own Bar Mitzvah and recalls his Bar Mitzvah speech.

A Bar Mitzvah was a great and glorious event at the home of Nahum Rabinowitz. Old Minde guided the many preparations.

Clothed in holiday best and wearing her precious kerchief, old Minde ruled the servants with an iron hand. Her slightest bidding was obeyed instantly. No one dared move hand or foot without her consent. She decided on such doubtful matters as who should be invited to the party, who should sit at the head of the table, which courses should be served first, which last. Even the Bar Mitzvah boy did not escape her scolding and bustling. She warned him not to chew his nails, not to giggle, not to act like a clown—in short, not to be his usual mischievous self.

"Since the Lord, blessed be He, has spared us in His abundant mercy and has preserved us and allowed us to see this day of days, the least *you* can do is improve your conduct and behave like a man." Thus she reproached the cause of all the festivities. And while she reprimanded him, she wet her fingers and smoothed his forelocks—the remnant she had saved from Nahum's intentions. For Nahum, her son, had wanted to cut them off entirely, but Minde stopped him.

"When my eyes are closed your sons will be yours," she told

him. "Then you may even make them gentiles, if you wish. But while I'm still alive, and as long as *I* breathe, I want to see God's image on their faces!"

A large crowd of friends accompanied Nahum Rabinowitz home after the synagogue service, with members of the entire family: Aunt Hannah and her sons, Uncle Pini and his sons, other relatives and friends.

Among those present was the teacher, Rabbi Moshe David Ruderman, dressed in his oversized Sabbath caftan and wearing a headgear of worn-out, time-faded plush. Self-effacing and forlorn, the Rabbi tried to curl up in a corner and lose himself. He spoke to no one; he barely touched the wine or the sweets. He sat desolate throughout the festivities, hunched over, inclining his head every now and then, covering his mouth with the folds of his caftan when he coughed.

At last the moment arrived: it was time for the Bar Mitzvah speech. The Bar Mitzvah boy climbed upon the table. Instantly the Rabbi's body straightened; he was awake and alert. His back was as straight as a ramrod, his bushy black eyebrows bristled, his sharp eyes met the eyes of his pupil, piercing them yet steadying them. His thumb, like the baton of an orchestra conductor, made a grand sweep upward. The sign to begin the speech had been given.

Atop the table, his pupil, the nervous, excited Bar Mitzvah boy, stood above the heads of his audience. Eyes watched him expectantly, waiting for the well-planned words to pour out. He became flustered, almost collapsed. Dark spots danced before his eyes, his knees shook, his tongue dried up, all his senses quivered. He felt as if he were walking on a delicate sheet of ice. In an instant the film would break, plunging him into the depths.

But the fear lasted only a moment. Glancing at the Rabbi and the sturdy sweep of his hand, the boy became calm. He began to speak, and his fear left him. His stage fright disappeared. His mind was crystal clear. His voice swelled and he felt as if he stood on a broad, unshakeable bridge of iron. He was confident, his excitement grew, a glow penetrated his entire body, warm and sweet, such as he had never before experienced. His words flowed like rich oil, smooth as if poured from a jar.

Throughout the crucial hour that the Bar Mitzvah boy preached from the table, he was given over wholly to the speech. Still, he could not take his eyes from his audience. They sat there, clinging to his words. He watched their faces, their gestures.

Nothing escaped him. Here was Isaac Avigdor, his shoulders twitching, his eyes spreading fear like a robber's. There stood old Joshua, believed to have reached one hundred years of age this very day, his tongue wagging in his toothless mouth like the clapper of a bell. Near him, eyes closed, head turned to one side, stood his son Berka, well advanced in years. Close at hand was Asher Neidis, a well-fleshed man, broad of bone and belly, his silk caftan bursting at the seams.

Over there was Yosi Fruchstein, whose open mouth showed large artificial teeth, whose spectacles reflected the rays of the sun, whose beard was cut short and sparse. People gossiped that he was a "free-thinker." He often played chess with Nahum Rabinowitz, and was known to read forbidden books like *Mysteries of Paris*. At his side stood his younger brother, Michael, shrewd and quicksilver-y, always belittling everyone and everything. It was common knowledge that he permitted his gentile maid to put out the lights on Friday evening, and that he hobnobbed with such "characters" as Moshe Berger and Buni Konover, men known from their very youth to overlook the close trim given to their beards by the barber.

Israel Benditzky was there too. Long ago he had been nicknamed "Israel the Fiddler," though now he owned a fine home and was president of a synagogue. Full-bearded, full-bodied, he was indeed an important man in the community. No one dared call him "Fiddler" any more, not even behind his back, yet to this very day, he would gladly play at weddings.

Even Raphael the sexton was in the audience. Tense and intent, his ears turned to the address like funnels, he sat with his thin face all screwed up, even his nose at attention. Any moment, it seemed, he would slap his hands on the table and cry out his familiar Sabbath singsong: "Ten gulden for Kohen!"

No one escaped the Bar Mitzvah's eyes. Not even his playmates, the mischief-makers who at the beginning had made faces to get him to laugh. Now they were motionless, their mouths open, silent, wondering, envying.

But more than anyone else in the group, there was Uncle Pini. He was dressed in a beautiful silk caftan tied around his full waist by a woven sash, and in blue satin headgear. With one eye closed, Uncle Pini peered upward from his place of honor at the head of the table. His lips wore a wise smile, as if he were chuckling knowingly into his long beard and saying: "This young scoundrel is doing all right—you can't deny the obvious. But does he *daven* every day? Does he wash his hands before meals? Does he say prayers at bedtime? Does he avoid carrying a burden on Sabbath? I doubt it!"

And directly in front of him the Bar Mitzvah boy saw his father's face, bright and shining, as if a new light had been cast on it. He appeared the happiest man alive. He stood erect; he was taller by several inches. His lips moved in rhythm with the lips of his son. His face was radiant, and his eyes moved over the audience, to his brother Pini, to the Rabbi, to the mother of the Bar Mitzvah boy.

And the mother, dear little Haya Esther! There she stood, modest, humble, amid the women. Her head was covered with the Sabbath kerchief. She was nervous, and she sighed softly as she crackled her knuckles. Two tears, shining in the rays of the sun, rolled down her pale white cheeks wrinkled long before their time.

Why the tears? Were they tears of joy, of happiness, of pride? Or were they tears of pain and sorrow for the hardships, the troubles that had come to the Rabinowitz family? Perhaps she hears a still small voice whisper inside her heart— the heart of a mother—that this young son, her Bar Mitzvah boy holding forth so bravely, so clearly, was destined soon to stand over her grave and recite the Kaddish for her departed soul?

Who can penetrate the mysteries of a mother's heart? Who can guess the source of her tears?

From **Haye Adam,** Vol. I, the Autobiography of Sholom Aleichem. New York. Shtibel: 1920; this selection translated by A. E

A charming book points up a small imperfection in an imperfect world. The writer recalls her sister's Confirmation in old San Francisco, and her father's violent reaction.

On the day of Addie's confirmation, the rabbi learned that Father did not fail to make known his contempt for the false witness, though he walked in high places, even upon the altar of the synagogue. It was customary for the confirmation class to present a gift to the rabbi at the conclusion of the exercises in recognition of his instruction. This year the speech of presentation had been awarded to a close friend of Addie's, Norma Samuels. We knew it by heart. For weeks Norma, curled up on our dining-room sofa, practiced inflections of fervor. "And to you, our kind and loving teacher, who have spared no pains toward our spiritual education, inculcating the true significance of the precepts of our beloved religion, we offer a slight token in remembrance of happy hours passed under your untiring guidance and loving ministration."

From his corner Father listened, savoring the cadence, respectful of the words of many syllables—"inculcating," "ministration"—and approving the sentiment of gratitude, echoing in his own blood the beat of youth, its aspiration and easy accomplishment.

Addie walked the halls committing her own address to memory. I did not approve of her interpretation, but felt constrained to accept the reading of Norma, because of our knowledge that the rabbi, leaving nothing to chance, had graciously written it.

The confirmation was achieved without misadventure. Boys and girls together discharged the Ten Commandments at the rabbi like a salvo, or came forward singly to declaim a prayer or protest a creed. Addie, in her turn, approached the altar rail; the tremolo of tears, always close to the surface when she was frightened, charged her voice with religious fervor, and she disclosed, as if it were a recent personal revelation, that "Truly the light is sweet and a pleasant thing it is for the eyes to behold the sun. Ecclesiastes, Chapter 2, Verse 7."

As she continued, Father's eyes were moist, and he drew a deep sigh of satisfaction, but not for long. At the close of the exercises Norma Samuels, garlands of daisies binding her auburn hair, rose and made her presentation. "And to you, our beloved teacher," she began, and Polly's lips and my own prompted her as she continued her measured way to a successful end.

"You have taken me by surprise, my dear Norma," the rabbi began, and Father needed to hear no more. To the remainder of the congregation, the words of the rabbi were the customary, gracious words of response to the customary speech of presentation. To Father's zealous ear, the rabbi had branded himself. "Liar! Taken by surprise!"

Never again did Father sit beneath the altar rail, sanctioning the word of that rabbi by his presence. Every Saturday morning, to the accompaniment of the solo which preceded the sermon, Father noisily replaced his book of prayer within the box beneath his pew and walked the full length of the synagogue to the exit, so that the world might witness his contempt for falsehood. Mother suffered under the public display but, up to the day the rabbi left the synagogue, no sermon of his reached the ear of Father.

From **920 O'Farrell Street,** by Harriet Lane Levy, New York: Doubleday and Company, 1947.

◄§ BAR MITZVAH ON THURSDAY by Charles An-goff ε◆ *David was to be Bar Mitzvah. It was 1915, in the United States, and the family was poor. There could be no Sabbath Bar Mitzvah; that was too expensive. According to Jewish law, it was permissible to admit a young man into the fold on Monday or Thursday as well as Sabbath. There would be no speech, of course, but to make it a festive occasion, David's parents planned a party on the following Sunday... The author is a prominent American Jewish writer and editor. This story is from the second volume, as yet unpublished, of a trilogy on the life of an immigrant family in the United States.*

◄§ The Thursday morning before the Thursday he was to be confirmed David was awakened very early to go with his father to the synagogue in order that he would see how another young boy was being confirmed, so that when David's turn came he would know precisely what to do. Hitherto David was permitted to say his morning prayers at home by himself. David was pleasantly surprised by what he witnessed in the synagogue that morning. In fact, he was rather moved by the stark and simple ceremony, and he began to wonder whether he shouldn't keep up his morning and afternoon and evening prayers after he himself was confirmed.

The following Thursday, which was the nearest Torah-reading weekday to his thirteenth birthday, David was awakened by his father about six-thirty in the morning. It was a chilly April morning, and David was very sleepy. But his father kept nudging him, and finally David opened his eyes. He at once remembered what day it was, and began to dress quickly. As he washed his face he wondered where his mother was. His father told him that she had rushed out to get some rolls, which the grocery delivery man had forgotten to leave. Somehow this disappointed David. It seemed like a very prosaic way to begin so important a day, and vaguely he felt as if he had been deliberately insulted by the grocery delivery man. Why, then, did he pick this day above all days to forget the rolls?

"Your mother thinks you're still a baby, even on this day, David," said his father with a strange note of sadness in his voice. "She wants you to have a good breakfast before you go to synagogue. Well, mothers always think their children are... children. But I must tell you that after today, when you say the morning prayers, you'll have to do so before eating breakfast. Religious duties must be attended to before eating or even taking a glass of water. But your teacher, no doubt, has already told you that. *Nu*, there's your mother...."

Nechame's face seemed rather flushed. It may have been the morning air, thought David, but then...it may be something else. Long, long ago David felt that his mother was a woman of deep feeling, not only about world matters, such as Zionism, which was very near to her, but about him and the other children, about Moshe, about parks and flowers, about the sunset and the sunrise, about the light of a street lamp seen from a distance on a rainy evening. He recalled how she stopped one rainy evening, when they were returning from Bobbe Leah's house, and she said to David, "Look at the beautiful lines the lamp way off there is making in the rain. It could be a boat on the ocean, passing our boat, or a lighthouse, or a *droshke* rushing past us."

Nechame rushed with preparing the breakfast for David: Moshe was going to pick up a bite at a kosher restaurant near his shop. He was afraid he'd be too late to return home. Nechame, on this day, got the special *boolkes* (rolls) that David liked, and also an onion roll with thick pieces of salt stuck on the sides. She hurriedly buttered two of the *boolkes* and the onion roll and poured a cup of cocoa. Nechame and Moshe sat down at the table, watching their oldest son eat. At one point Moshe told Nechame to have a bite herself, but she said that she didn't feel like eating just yet. David looked up several times, and saw that both his parents were looking lovingly at him. He felt a warm feeling go through him, but he also felt somewhat embarrassed for a reason that he didn't quite understand. Nechame was overflowing with emotion, as was Moshe. She hardly knew what to do or say. After a while she merely said, "*Nu*, David, you really don't have to rush so. Father spoke to the *shames*, so I guess they'll wait. Besides, it's a little chilly outside, and you'll need a good breakfast, even though the walk from here to the synagogue isn't so much."

"Yes, there really is no hurry, I mean too much of a hurry," said Moshe. "*Nu*, David, if you want another *boolke*, have one. How much time does it take to eat another *boolke*?"

David said he had eaten enough, and he and his father began to walk out. At that moment Nechame walked over to David, got hold of his arm with both her hands, and pressed David's arm close to her breast. "*Nu*, my son, a *guten mazel tov* to you. You should live to be 120 years. And...and afterward you'll come back and have another cup of cocoa. You always have two cups on a cold morning." This recalled to David a time the preceding winter when he first asked for a second cup of cocoa, because it was so cold outside, and ever since then his mother had been asking him every morning whether he didn't want a second cup. Generally he didn't, and he remembered, at the moment with shame, how once he said, rather crossly, to his mother, "How many times are you going to ask me if I want another cup? If I want one I'll ask for one. You don't have to ask me the same question every morning. Gee!"

This time David said, "Yes, mother, I think I will have another later."

David and his father said nothing to each other as they went to the Synagogue. They went to the basement, where the weekday services were held. His first reaction was one of revulsion at the musty smell. After a while, however, he got used to it. He had imagined that the older folk would greet him, but not one of them said a word. David was the only one of his general age at the services. There were only about twenty of the older folk, or two *minyans*. This, too, disappointed David. He had no reason for thinking so, or for imagining so, but he did expect the downstairs chapel of the synagogue to be filled for his Bar Mitzvah. It was his first—and not his last—realization that what was important to him could be of no importance whatever to nearly everybody else in the world.

The first part of the service began and David participated as a member of the congregation. Then the Torah was taken out of the holy ark, and Moshe gently pushed David near to the rostrum, toward the center of the hall. Then David was called to the Torah, where, after putting around his shoulder a holy shawl, he read a small section of Holy Writ, and the *shamus* then took over, hardly paying any attention to David. Before

David realized what had happened the Torah was back in the ark, and in little more than ten minutes the entire service was over. His father awkwardly shook his hand, and said, "*Nu*, you're a man now, a real Jew and may you be a good one, a joy to Israel and to your mother and me and your family." Four members of the Congregation came up to David and mechanically congratulated him. The others apparently were in too much of a hurry to get to their businesses to do likewise. When Moshe and David were outside, Moshe said, "*Nu*, my son, I have to go to the shop. It's still rather early for you. So go home, and I'll see you tonight," and he was off.

David slowly turned to return home. He had a heavy heart. He was filled with bitter and sharp disappointment. He had just gone through an important part of his life, and he felt he was robbed of something. He had expected more emotional commotion, more ceremony, more people present and talking and making a fuss over him, a deeper feeling of change...instead he got this. He couldn't understand it. Was all life this way? He was a grown-up now, he could help form a *minyan*, he was a full-fledged member of Israel, God would from now on keep a close watch on his every deed and apportion reward and punishment, yet he felt no different from before. If anything, he felt less important than before. Before he was a recognized member of the pre-Bar-Mitzvah group of boys, and people, of late, constantly talked of his coming Bar-Mitzvah. Now they would not have that to talk about...and he would be nothing. He knew his father had to go to work, but he resented his going to work this morning. Why didn't he at least walk back to the house with him? Why didn't his mother wait outside the synagogue for him? Why didn't somebody do something? Why did they leave him all alone on this cold April morning?

And yet, despite these sad thoughts, David felt closer to Judaism than he had felt for a long, long time. The more he thought of what he had been robbed, the more attracted he felt toward it, though he couldn't really put any of these thoughts into words. He thought of the splendor of the Saturday service, of the singing of the cantor and the choir boys, of the magnificence of the huge holy ark, of all the people, the men downstairs and the women upstairs, of the holiday spirit pervading the entire synagogue—and as he thought of all these matters, he loved them more and more, and he was ashamed that he had ever, even for an instant, considered going away from them. And he was a bit angry at his parents for not arranging to have his Bar-Mitzvah on the Sabbath. He knew that a ceremony on the Sabbath meant a considerable expense, and he appreciated his father's economic situation, still...there were some things that parents did for their children, no matter how much they cost. And as he entertained these thoughts he was sorry for thinking them. This was no way to begin his full manhood, his admission to the company of full-fledged Jews: thinking ill of one's parents. Such thoughts, indeed, were specifically forbidden, not merely by the rabbis and by common sense, but by the Bible—yes, by one of the Ten Commandments. ...All of which made him very lonely. And the emptiness of the streets only intensified his loneliness. He heard a milk wagon from a nearby street, and off in the distance he saw a policeman and several men rushing to work. But he didn't know a single one of these people, even by sight. And he saw not one of his playmates. Of course, it was very early...But the whole world seemed to conspire to have him alone on this one morning when he was in need of companionship of some sort.

As he got closer to his house he felt a bit better. At least the buildings were familiar, and when he entered the hallway of his own house, he smelled familiar smells—rolls being toasted, cocoa and coffee and tea being made, and he heard familiar voices, some from his own family and others from upstairs and in a neighboring house, and a new, refreshing warmth enveloped him. As he came into the house, he was pretty much himself again. His brothers and sisters were still asleep. But his mother seemed to be brighter than he had seen her for a long, long time. She patted his head and shoulders and then hugged him, which both embarrassed him and pleased him. His Bar-Mitzvah was not without notice. He looked again at his mother and he noticed that she was dressed in her Saturday clothes and obviously had combed her hair with special care. She escorted him to the table, where he noted there was a cup all ready to be filled for him, and beside the cup was, not a roll, but a piece of cake and some jam. He was delighted and he looked and looked at what was before him.

"You like cake and jam, don't you, David?" said his mother.

"Yes," he mumbled.

"So have it, David. It's your Bar-Mitzvah. It's not much, but today there is no time, you have to go to school and everything. But on Sunday, like your father and I promised you, we'll have a little party for you. Everybody will be here. Then there will be more cake . . . and everything, David. So eat."

She poured some cocoa into the cup and stirred it for him. He began to sip the cocoa and eat the cake and jam, and he felt a strange combined feeling, one of loneliness and being among a host of men and women. Only he and his mother were in the room, but it seemed to him as if there were thousands of people there with them, all of them smiling at him and watching him eat, all of them Jews, some with holy shawls, others in their street clothes, and there were also some young boys and young girls, and he seemed to hear singing, from a cantor and choir, and the room became like the upstairs section of the synagogue, which was used for the Sabbath services, and he could see the magnificent holy ark and he felt the soft warmth of the services and the silent prayer of the congregation, and the gradual shuffling of feet here and there, signifying that the silent stand-ing prayer had been concluded by several people, who were waiting for the others to conclude their prayer, and for the cantor to proceed with the services.

David drank more of the cocoa and ate more of the cake and jam. "Very good, mother," he said.

These words were what his mother was waiting for. Her son was happy with what she had done for him, and both of them felt that his Thursday early morning Bar-Mitzvah had been rescued from its cold anonymity and oblivion.

Suddenly David decided to be the big man of the family. He felt called upon to make his mother feel that not only was he not downhearted by the lack of ceremony, but that he loved it. "The services in the synagogue were very nice," he said. "I knew my prayers very well. I didn't hesitate once."

"That's good, David," said his mother. "I knew you'd have no difficulty."

"Huh," he smiled. "What is there about it that can be diffi-cult? It's like any other prayer, and besides, I've said it hun-dreds of times. And," he added abruptly, "it's much better this way than with a speech and all that fuss. A Jew is a Jew in his heart, like my Hebrew teacher said. He doesn't need to make a speech to tell people he's a Jew. Like this it's simpler and nicer, really, mother."

His mother patted his head and had to control herself from crying.

"Of course, David, of course. But we'll have a nice party on Sunday."

"All right," he said nonchalantly, and his mother was at peace again, and all the horrible thoughts of inadequacy that had assailed her while her son and her husband were in synagogue this all-important morning had vanished.

On the way to school, which was just around the corner, he felt elated, more grown-up than he had ever felt before. He was proud to be a Jew, a full grown member of the Jewish community, and he was going to see to it that the Jewish race would be proud of him. Who knows but that someday he would be a hero in Israel, like Bar Kochba, or maybe he would carry on the work of Theodor Herzl. Yes, his father, he knew, didn't approve of Zionism, but he had a sneaking suspicion that if he, David, should become as prominent as Herzl, his father wouldn't mind at all....

And he thought and thought...and soon he seemed to hear the beautiful melody of *Alice Blue Gown*, and he bathed himself in its sad sweetness, and he kept on hearing it and he hoped it would pour into his ears and heart for a long, long time....And then he heard more wonderful melodies, as if coming from a hurdy-gurdy, like the one that came to his neighborhood very often in the late afternoon and played and played all those grand Italian melodies *O Sole Mio, The Pearl Fishers, Pagliacci,* and made him feel so sad and good and pessimistic about life and also optimistic and spread a soft and hazy mystery over all creation and for a while made everything seem so far removed from him, even his own parents then seemed like pleasant strangers, not like parents.

The party the following Sunday was a bit of an anti-climax for David, at least at the beginning. To his parents, however, it was a milestone in their lives, and after a while David was infected with their enthusiasm and happiness and with the excitement of the entire gathering. All the relatives, naturally, were invited, and it was a miracle that they managed to get into Moshe's small apartment.

All the guests greeted and congratulated David when they entered, and also gave him his present, but thereafter they hardly noticed him, except to pat him on the head if he happened to pass by. At first this made him feel out of the picture, but when he realized that his Bar-Mitzvah was the cause of all this commotion he felt important again, especially when he overheard his father and several of the other menfolk remark about his brilliance in both Hebrew school and American school.

Indeed, what pleased him most about this celebration was the watch his father and mother gave him as a Bar-Mitzvah present. It was a gold Waltham watch, with an inscription on the back reading, "To our son, David, on his Bar Mitzvah, from his Father and Mother." They gave it to him just before the guests came. Moshe called his little family over to the kitchen table, and in a strangely shy manner said, "*Nu*, it is fitting, son, that we have our own little party before the others come, and your mother and I—and the other children, too, including little Benjamin—have got you a watch. Carry it with health for 120 years." Then he handed him the little box with the watch. David was embarrassed, and had a difficult time keeping from crying. As he was still opening the package his mother hugged him hurriedly and kissed him on his cheek. David wanted to hug her back and kiss her for a long, long time, but he didn't for some strange, compelling reason. For years and years after that he deeply regretted that he didn't give in to his impulse. David had hoped he would get a watch. His friends had got watches on their Bar-Mitzvahs. A watch was a sort of badge of reaching manhood among Jewish young boys. Most important of all, however, for David, was the mere fact that it was a watch, a real watch that ticked, whose hands moved, a watch that told time. A watch, to him, was one of the miracles of creation.

When he finally beheld the watch his heart overflowed with wonderment and gratitude. He struggled with himself as to what to say, and finally managed to say only, "Thank you, Father and Mother. I like it." He read the inscription. Then he put the watch in his watch pocket on the right side of his short pants. With the watch came a watch fob—made of leather, with a metal medal attached to the end. The medal was stamped with the seal of Boston. David couldn't understand the Latin, but the seal looked familiar and the word *Bostoniensis* assured him that it was the seal.

"What do those words say, David?" asked his father. "They don't look like English words, but who am I to know?"

"I don't think they're English," said David. "Latin. We haven't studied Latin yet."

"No?"

"That they study in high school," said David.

"Good," said his father. "That means you'll study it, too. Very much I don't know about it. But Dr. Kahn, *olav hasholem*, once told me that prescriptions were written in Latin, and that in college everybody had to study Latin, professional people of all kinds use it. So it's a good thing to know. *Nu*," he smiled, "you can begin studying Latin with this thing...."

"Watch fob, they call it," said David.

"Whatever it is. As long as you study it. Your mother and I thought it was pretty, so we picked it."

For the next several hours, indeed, for the duration of the party, David kept on taking the watch out of his pocket and looking at it. Several times he went to the bathroom in the hall for the sole purpose of admiring the watch all by himself, unhindered by the fear that someone might see him or might interrupt him. But the closer he got to the watch, so to speak, the greater did a certain worry become in his eye; the deprivation that his father had subjected himself and the family at large to in order to buy the watch. David was thus both delighted and downcast. For a while he was also angry at his father for burdening him with financial worries, but he quickly realized that these worries were generated entirely by himself, that his father had nothing directly to do with his mental state. The more David thought in this direction the sorrier was he that he had ever harbored any unworthy thoughts about his father, and as he looked at his watch he didn't know how to expiate for his thoughts. He was glad that relatives didn't bother him with too many questions, for he was so mixed up that he wasn't sure he would know how to answer them.

◆§ AN EXTRAORDINARY BAR MITZVAH by Philip S. Bernstein ℰ➤ *Amid the ruins of Frankfurt in 1947, Rabbi Philip Bernstein, Adviser on Jewish Affairs to the American Military Government, and one of the prominent leaders of American Jewry, addressed his son, who was Bar Mitzvah that day.*

◆§ This is an extraordinary Bar Mitzvah.

Stephen chose it so. He had been trained for his confirmation in Rochester during the month of November, but when he learned that my responsibilities would keep me here longer he decided to postpone the event, to learn a new portion and to have the service far from his own friends and our families in the normal, peaceful environment of our community, so as to share it with me and with you. You will forgive me, therefore, a pardonable sense of gratification and pride on this blessed occasion.

This must be also a very extraordinary and heart stirring event for many of the Jews who are here this morning. The very fact that no Bar Mitzvah has been held in Frankfurt since 1940, the very fact that since liberation there was not a single Jewish boy in this once-great city of Frankfurt who reached the age of thirteen, tells more forcefully than I could dare put into words what happened to the Jewish children. This very building in which we gather was once a Jewish school, alive with the voices and activities of Jewish boys and girls. Stephen, then, becomes the symbol of the childhood that was and is no more.

This must be a poignant occasion, also, for the surviving members of the Jewish community of Frankfurt. This was one of the great Jewish communities of the world. The Judaism of Frankfurt, which combined the noblest of our tradition with modern enlightenment, was renowned throughout the world. The very fact that we could find no adequate standing synagogue in which to conduct this ceremony reveals the fate of Judaism here. Frankfurt was the home of great Jewish families who combined material success and patriotism with devotion to their faith. Here the Rothschild family flourished. Here the Speyer family made possible the modern University of Frankfurt. From this community came Dr. Paul Ehrlich who helped mankind toward freedom from one of its most devastating scourges.

It is of special significance that this hall in which we meet was the last institution used by the Jewish community for religious services from 1942 until liberation by the American Army. On November 10, 1938, the synagogues of Frankfurt were desecrated, burned, destroyed. The Jewish community then conducted its services in this hall of this school. Here, in these bitter years between 1938 and 1942, with ominous, black clouds gathering overhead and irresistibly pressing down upon them, the remaining members of this community assembled to worship God according to the traditions of their fathers, and to seek strength to withstand their oppressors, and to find solace for their losses.

But, in the fall of 1942, the end came. Then began the deportations to Litzmannstadt, Lodz, where they were imprisoned in the ghetto and, ultimately, exterminated. At this point, services were discontinued in the Philantropin Building. There was a brief period of a few weeks when they were conducted in a private home. Then the Gestapo ordered them to cease entirely. For three years there were no Jewish religious exercises in Frankfurt, save for the anguished prayers that must have welled up from the heart of the miserable, terror-stricken people.

Even the very physical circumstances under which we meet today are extraordinary. This is now a hospital for German war-wounded. Some of the very men who participated in these dreadful things are now round-about. There is a window in which the *Magen David*, the Star of David, has been defaced by some Nazi hand.

Yes, we are surrounded by memories today, by tragic memories of a greatness that was and is no more, and of a people who are no longer among the living.

But, that is of the past. The very fact that we are gathered here to worship this morning is a source of hope for the future. On every side you see the wages of the terrible sin which was here committed by the mighty and the wicked. Our eyes confirm the rightness of the prophetic words which Stephen just read to us:

> For the sword hath devoured round about thee.
> Why is the strong one overthrown?
> He stood not because the Lord did thrust him down.

The oppressor may triumph for a moment. He may enjoy for a short time the rewards of his gangsterism, but his house is built on sand. It cannot stand against the wrath of the Lord.

It cannot withstand the irresistible moral laws of history. But Israel survives. This very Bar Mitzvah in these very extraordinary circumstances demonstrates the indestructibility of our people and our faith. *"Am Yisrael Chai."*

In the prophetic portion that was just read, the Lord says, "Fear not, for I am with thee." That is a magnificent promise and an imperishable source of hope. It is also justification for pride. It makes me proud I am a Jew. Despite the misfortunes of my people, I would not exchange that heritage for anything in the world.

It is this heritage which we formally transmit to you today, Stephen. When I place my hands upon your head in benediction, I will be the humble instrument through which will flow the stream of history and memories of the great and the good in Israel, the ideals and the aspirations of our people, the strength and the lift of our faith. It is something which places upon you a solemn responsibility to be worthy of its precepts, to be loyal to its ideals, and to express them in a life of service.

"So be the Lord with you as I will let you go."

From **What the Jews Believe,** by Philip S. Bernstein, New York: Farrar, Straus, and Young, 1951.

BAR MITZVAH PRIMER

The question was asked:

"How can we overcome the Jewish people?"

And it was said:

"Go up and down before their Houses of Study and Houses of Worship. If you do not hear the voices of their children chanting, you can overcome them. But if you hear the chant of children, you can never sub-due them."

From the Midrash

⊷§ The Jews have always been known as the "people of the book." Among their many great books, the book of prayers stands out as a cherished companion in everyday life.

Long ago, people worshiped God through the sacrifice of animals, or even human beings. In the long history of religion, the Jews were the first to change from such worship to more civilized forms. For sacrifice we substituted prayers; for the burning of incense we searched our hearts and thanked God for His wonders and His goodness.

At the beginning, prayer was private, unorganized. One prayed at any time, in any place, in any words. Eventually prayer became public, organized. We prayed at definite times, in houses of worship, in definite words.

The Hebrew word *siddur* means order, arrangement. Our prayer book, the Siddur, is an orderly collection of prayers, arranged according to the ancient practices of our people. Some of it—for example, the *Shema*—was composed over two thousand years ago. Other parts—the Friday evening prayer *Lekha Dodi*—were written just a few hundred years ago. Many modern prayer books include new readings and prayers. Most of the Siddur is in Hebrew, but there are selections in Aramaic, a language spoken during the days of the Second Temple in Babylonia. Different parts of the world have their different versions of the Siddur, but nearly all are based on the one compiled around 870 C. E. by Rabbi Amram, a great Babylonian scholar.

The Siddur has marched with the Jewish people through twelve centuries of existence. It has been with us at births and at deaths, on Sabbaths and on workdays, in times of joy, and in times of sorrow. It has changed to meet the changing needs of the people. Its prayers are not only requests to God; they are prayers of thanks, the confession of sins, the reminder of great events in our long history, the passages from the Bible, the Talmud, and other writings, and the great and original poetry of the Jewish people, the expression of its deepest feeling.

Maimonides, the sage of the Middle Ages, said: "Come to your Siddur as if it held great treasure, and pray 'with deep feeling'."

৺ THE SYNAGOGUE ৶

৺ When the Jewish people were exiled from their own land after the destruction of the First Temple (568 B.C.E.) they no longer had the Temple at Jerusalem as the center for their religious observance. In Babylon, we find the synagogue becoming an institution. The word "synagogue" derives from a Greek word meaning "place of assembly." But the synagogue was not only a place of assembly. It was also a house of learning and a house of worship. It was within this institution that a new form of religious observance grew up: prayer.

From these beginnings, religious observances as we know them in Western civilization developed. The forms adopted by the Jewish people became the source from which other religions drew, until today there is not a place in the Western World where a house of worship cannot be found. There men gather together to pray to God.

The synagogue has often meant much more than this to its community. It has been the center of a man's life. Here prayers were said when he was born; here he studied as a child; here he was Bar Mitzvah; here he studied as a man; here he was married; here he celebrated the birth of his children; here he helped the needy; and here too he remembered those who died. All this he did, not alone, but with his family and friends, in his community and in its synagogue.

A synagogue can be formed by any ten men. They can meet in any structure. As we know it today, it is often a large institution, composed of many hundreds of families who have elected a rabbi to serve as their spiritual leader. Whether it is large or small, in it there is an Ark containing the Torah, over which burns steadily the Eternal Light.

⊷ THE TALLIT AND THE TEFILLIN ⊱

⊷ Hear, O Israel, the Lord our God, the Lord is One.

And thou shalt love the Lord thy God with all thy heart, and with all thy soul, and with all thy might. And these words, which I command thee this day, shall be upon thy heart; and thou shalt teach them diligently unto thy children, and shalt talk of them when thou sittest in thy house, and when thou walkest by the way, and when thou liest down, and when thou risest up. And thou shalt bind them for a sign upon thy hand, and they shall be for frontlets between thine eyes. And thou shalt write them upon the door-posts of thy house, and upon thy gates.

Deuteronomy 6:4-9

And the Lord spoke unto Moses, saying: "Speak unto the children of Israel, and bid them that they make them throughout their generations fringes in the corners of their garments, and that they put with the fringe of each corner a thread of blue. And it shall be unto you for a fringe, that ye may look upon it, and remember all the commandments of the Lord, and do them; and that ye go not about after your own heart and your own eyes, after which ye use to go astray; that ye may remember and do all My commandments, and be holy unto your God. I am the Lord your God, who brought you out of the land of Egypt, to be your God: I am the Lord your God."

Numbers 15:37-41

These portions of the Bible, with their commandments to love and honor God, have given rise to certain observances faithfully followed today by traditional Jewry: the binding on of Tefillin, or phylacteries, and the wearing of the Tallit, or prayer shawl. Daily the Jew is thus reminded to love the Lord and obey His commandments. The young man begins these observances when he is Bar Mitzvah. Every day, at the Morning Service, with the exception of the Sabbath and Festivals, the phylacteries are bound on the arm, and then on the head, while the appropriate blessings and prayers are recited. Every day of the year the white prayer shawl with its blue or black stripes, is worn at the Morning Service.

These are not injunctions that govern man's relationship to man, as do so many of the teachings of the Bible. Rather do they deal with man's relationship to God, symbolic reminders in everyday life of one's religious convictions. They are part of the ritual that is often a concrete expression of religious experience.

⋖§ THE SABBATH ξ⋗

⋖§ Each week of our lives, there comes a day of rest. For the Jews, Saturday; for the Gentile, Sunday; for the Mohammedan, Friday.

This day of rest, this Sabbath, is a unique Jewish contribution to the life of all peoples of the world. It began in the days of the Bible. The Ten Commandments tell us: "Remember the Sabbath Day, to keep it holy." For on the seventh day of the Creation, God finished His work, and He rested. So man, too, rests from his labors on this seventh day. And because we once were slaves in Egypt, and were freed, we must have a rest-day for ourselves, and our servants, and the "stranger within our gates."

These two ideas have been an important part of Judaism from its very beginnings. Man was created in the image of God; the Sabbath is a reminder of the godlike and spiritual qualities of man. And the Sabbath is a symbol of freedom; just as the Jewish people were given a Sabbath from their slavery in Egypt, so must each of us have freedom from personal labor.

From Bible times, too, comes the Sabbath year, the sabbatical. Every seven years, a field lay fallow and rested from its work of producing grain and food. This ancient notion became an important part of modern, scientific agriculture.

Sabbath observance has many forms and, within Judaism itself, a large variety of customs. Deepest is the thought of Sabbath as a source of rest and inspiration, a time for prayer and singing, a renewal for the coming week. In quiet study, in the gatherings of friends and families, the Sabbath finds expression today. So taken for granted is this custom among all the civilized world, in every religion, that we do not pause to think how strange, how hurried, how oppressive, our lives would be without our weekly Sabbath.

Ahad Ha'am, one of the great Jewish thinkers of modern times, wrote: "A Jew who feels a real tie with the life of his people throughout the generations will find it utterly impossible to think of the existence of Israel without the Sabbath. One can say without exaggeration that even more than Israel has kept the Sabbath, the Sabbath has kept Israel."

◈§ THE CHILD IN JEWISH LIFE by Solomon Schechter ƺ⮝
*How old is the custom of Bar Mitzvah? What role did the child
play in Jewish life? When did a boy actually assume the religious duties of Judaism? These are some of the questions that
Solomon Schechter, one of the great names in Jewish theology
and scholarship at the turn of the twentieth century, discusses.*

◈§ The origin of the Bar Mitzvah ceremony...cannot claim a
very high antiquity....As far as the Bible goes, there is not
the slightest indication of the existence of such a ceremony.
...It was only in the times of the Rabbis that the date of
thirteen was fixed as giving the boy his majority. But it would
be a mistake to think that before having obtained this majority
the boy was considered as under age in every respect. Certainly
the law made every possible effort to connect him with the
synagogue, and to initiate him in his religious duties long before the age of thirteen.

The boy's first appearance in the synagogue was at the beginning of the fourth year. There was no better reason for this
attendance either in the Temple or in the synagogue than that
the parents might be rewarded by God for the trouble of taking
their children there. In later times there was another excuse for
taking the little children to the synagogue. They were there
allowed to sip the wine of the Sanctification Cup, which was
the exclusive privilege of the children; an easy way of wor-
shipping, but, as you can observe, it is a method that they
enjoy and understand most excellently. They did not less enjoy
and understand the service with which they were charged on
the day of "The Rejoicing of the Law." On this feast they were

provided with flags, which they carried before the bearers of the Torah, who feasted them after the service with sweets. Another treat was that of being called up on this day to the Torah, a custom that is still practiced. A beautiful custom was that every Sabbath, after finishing the weekly lesson and dressing the Scroll of the Law, the children used to come up to the *Almemor* (pulpit) and kiss the Torah. Leaving the Synagogue they kissed the hands of the scholars.

At home the initiation began with the blessing the child received on every eve of the Sabbath, and with its instruction in the *Sh'ma* (Hear O Israel) and other verses. Short prayers, consisting of a single sentence, were also chosen for children of this age. The function of the child on the eve of the first day of Passover is well known. Besides the putting of the four questions for the meaning of the strange ceremony (Exod. 13: 14), the boy had also to recite, or rather to sing, the *Hallel*, "Praise." But I am afraid that they enjoyed better the song of "One Kid," which was composed or rather adapted for their special entertainment from an old German poem.

Within three or four years after entering the synagogue, and with the growth of intellect and strength, the religious duties of the boy increased and became of a more serious character. He had not only to attend the school, which was troublesome enough, but he was also expected to attend the services more regularly, and to gain something by it. Yet the Rabbis were not so tyrannical as to put unjust demands on the patience of the child. Thus we read in the Tractate *Sopherim* that according to the law the portion of the week, after having been recited in Hebrew, must be translated into the language of the country for the benefit of the unlearned people, the women, and the children. Another consideration children experienced from the Rabbis was that at the age of nine or ten the boy was initiated into the observance of the Day of Atonement by fasting a few hours. Lest, however, this good work might be overdone, and thus endanger the child's health, the sage Rabbi Acha used to tell his congregation after the *Musaf* prayer "My brethren, let every one of you who has a child go home and make it eat...."

With his advancing age, not only the boy's duties but also his rights were increased. An enumeration of all these rights would lead me too far, but I shall mention the custom which allowed the boy the recital of *"Kaddish"* and *"Borkhu"* in the synagogue. Now this privilege is restricted to the orphan boy. It is interesting to hear that girls were also admitted to recite the *Kaddish* in the synagogue, in cases where their parents left no male children. In some countries the boy had the exclusive privilege of reading the prayers on the evenings of the festivals and Sabbaths.... As to the question whether the boy, while under age, might lawfully be considered as one of the Ten when such a *minyan* was required, or one of the three in the case of grace after meals, I can only say that the authorities never agreed in this respect. Whilst the one insisted upon his having become Bar Mitzvah, the other was satisfied with his showing such signs of intelligence as would enable him to participate in the ceremony in question. Here is an instance of such a sign. Abaye and Raba, the two celebrated heroes of the Babylonian Talmud, were sitting at the table of Rabbah. Before saying grace he asked them, "Do you know to whom these prayers are addressed?" Thereupon one boy pointed to the roof, whilst the other boy went out and pointed to the sky. The examiner was satisfied with their answer.

The privilege of putting on the phylacteries forms now in most countries the chief distinction of "The Son of the Law"; in olden times, however, every boy had claim to it as soon as he showed himself capable of behaving respectfully when wearing the holy symbol. It even happened that certain honours of the synagogue were bestowed on boys, though under age. We possess a copy of a Jewish epitaph dating from about the third century, which was written in Rome for a boy of eight years, who is there designated as trustee. The fact is the more curious, as on the other hand the Palestinian Rabbi Abuha, who lived in the same century, maintained that no man must be elected as trustee before he has achieved his fiftieth year.

From all these remarks it will easily be seen that in olden times the boy enjoyed almost all the rights of majority long before the day of his being "The Son of the Law." The Talmud, the Gaonim, and even Rabbi Isaac Alfasi and Maimonides knew neither the term "The Son of the Law" (in our sense of the word) nor any ceremony connected with it. There is only one slight reference to such an institution, recorded in the Tractate *Sopherim*. We read there: "In Jerusalem there was the godly custom to initiate the children at the beginning of the thirteenth year by fasting the whole Day of Atonement. During this year they took the boy to the priests and learned men that they might bless him, and pray for him that God might think him worthy of a life devoted to the study of the Torah and pious works." For, this author says, " they were beautiful, and their lives harmonious and their hearts directed to God."

Selected from **Studies in Judaism**, First Series, by Solomon Schechter, Philadelphia: Jewish Publication Society of America, 1896.

◄§ **PRAYER** §► *Prayer can be old and traditional or prayer can be new. It can be the original and heartfelt thought of any one of us, or the ancient and prescribed form of worship. Two prayers for the Bar Mitzvah follow: one old, and one quite new. . . .*

◄§ My God, God of my fathers, in truth and single-heartedness I lift my eyes to Thee on this great and solemn day. I have been a Jew from my birth; but on this day I voluntarily reenter Thy community of Israel. Henceforth it is my duty to keep Thy commandments, and I now become responsible for my own actions and I alone am answerable for them to Thee.

Before all men I glory in Thy name by which we of Israel are called. I pray unto Thee, heavenly Father; hearken to my heartfelt prayer: Pour out on me the bounty of Thy blessings, so that all my days may be full and fruitful because of the rich spiritual blessings which Thou canst shower upon me. Save me from evil impulse, and dispose my heart to love and revere Thee. Teach me the way of Thy commandments and lead me in their path. Take me by the hand and uphold me, that I do not stumble on the way on which this day I am first setting my steps. Give me strength to keep Thy holy Torah and Thy commands in the keeping of which is life, and through all my days may I proclaim glad and unafraid my profession of faith:

"Hear, O Israel, the Lord is our God, the Lord is One."

Composed by Haham Benjamin Artom; from the **Book of Prayer,** edited and translated by David de Sola Pool, Union of Sephardic Congregations, 1941.

⋖ BAR MITZVAH PRAYER From the Great Synagogue of Tel Aviv ⋗

⋖ Blessed be the God of Israel, Who has kept me alive and well to see this day of my Bar Mitzvah.

With His help, and of my own free choice, I stand today before the Torah. I greet this congregation of Israel, which began in the days of the Patriarchs, and which will live to see Israel redeemed and mankind at peace, as our prophets have foretold.

I make this solemn pledge to my people, Israel:

I will be faithful to my people, to our Torah, our faith, our common hopes. I will share in our burdens, and work for our salvation. I will help redeem and rebuild our homeland.

I pray that I may stand the test honorably and well, in a spirit of love and brotherhood for my own people, and in a spirit of truth and justice toward all who are created in the image of God.

My heart gives thanks to our Father in Heaven, Who has shielded me from evil and brought me safely to this day. I give heartfelt thanks to my parents, for bringing me up in the spirit of Truth and in the law of Truth, and for sowing a pleasant seed in my heart. My thanks and blessings, also, to all those who love me, to my relatives and friends; and to all the Household of Israel, from its beginnings even to its eternal future.

315

❧ CANTILLATION FOR TORAH READINGS ❧

✣ CANTILLATION FOR THE HAFTARAH ✢

Mah-pah pash-ta za-kef ka-ton za-kef ga-dol

mer-ha tip-ha mu-nah et-nah-tah mu-nah zar-ka mu-nah se - gol

mu-nah, mu-nah, r'vi-ee Par-zer

Tli-sha k'-ta - nah Tli-sha g'-do - lah

kad-ma v'-az- lah az-la ge-resh ger-sha-yim

dar-ga t'-vir y'-tiv ka-ton

sof pa-suk (or) sof pa-suk (at the end of The Haftorah)

IN FAREWELL

When the masters left the house of Rabbi Ammi...
 some say it was the house of Rabbi Hanina
 ...they said to him:
May you find your world in your lifetime,
and your future be realized in the life of
 the world to come,
your hope throughout the generations.
May your heart meditate in understanding,
your mouth speak wisdom,
your tongue move in songs of jubilation,
your eyelids look straight before you,
your eyes be alight with the light of the Torah,
and your face shine with the glow of the firmament;
may your lips utter knowledge,
and your reins rejoice uprightly,
and your footsteps hasten to hear the words of
 the Ancient of Days.

From the Midrash

⋅⋖§ ACKNOWLEDGMENTS §⋗⋅

The editor wishes to thank the following authors, translators, copyright holders, and publishers for their permission to reprint or translate the stories and excerpts from the volumes listed below.

American Zionist Youth Commission, **The Messenger from the Holy Land,** by S. Y. Agnon.

Charles Angoff, **Bar Mitzvah on Thursday.**

Helen Atkin and the Pioneer Woman, **My Name is Hayim,** by Moshe Prager.

Behrman House, Inc., **Pirke Aboth: Sayings of the Fathers,** by Joseph J. Hertz.

Philip S. Bernstein, **What the Jews Believe.**

Bloch Publishing Company, **Why I Am a Jew,** by Edmond Fleg.

Elijah Bortniker, **Three Men.**

Yehuda Burla, **A Caucasian Bar Mitzvah.**

Commentary Magazine, **An Orthodox GI Fights a War.**

Dial Press, **The Forgotten Ally,** by Pierre Van Paassen.

Doubleday and Company, **920 O'Farrell Street,** by Harriet Lane Levy.

Harold Friedman, **What Is Your Name?**

Lili Frishman, **The Tallit Weaver of Bagdad; Three Who Ate,** by David Frishman.

Roland B. Gittelsohn, **In Memoriam: Iwo Jima**

Haboneh Magazine, **Bar Mitzvah Joy,** by David Cohen.

Hebrew Publishing Company, **And It Came to Pass,** by Hayyim Nahman Bialik.

Jewish Publication Society of America, **The Democracy of Torah,** by Milton Konvitz; **Harvest in the Desert,** by Maurice Samuel; **Hebrew Ethical Wills,** edited by Israel Abrahams; selections from the Bible from **The Holy Scriptures; The Ma'aseh Book,** by Moses Gaster; **Studies in Judaism,** by Solomon Shechter.

Jewish Education Committee of New York, **Honest Scales,** by Asher Barash.

I. M. Lask, **The Three-Fold Covenant,** by Yehuda Yaari.

Meyer Levin, **Thrice He Laughed.**

Ludwig Lewisohn, **The Island Within.**

The Menorah Journal, **The Prayerbook.**

Howard C. Myers, Jr., **A Parable Against Persecution,** by Benjamin Franklin.

Moshe Nathanson, **Cantillations.**

David de Sola Pool, **Prayer** by Benjamin Artom.